INTERNATIONAL
EXPRESS

Workbook
Pre-Intermediate

Mike Macfarlane

OXFORD
UNIVERSITY PRESS

OXFORD
UNIVERSITY PRESS

Great Clarendon Street, Oxford OX2 6DP

Oxford University Press is a department of the University of Oxford.
It furthers the University's objective of excellence in research, scholarship,
and education by publishing worldwide in

Oxford New York

Auckland Cape Town Dar es Salaam Hong Kong Karachi
Kuala Lumpur Madrid Melbourne Mexico City Nairobi
New Delhi Shanghai Taipei Toronto

With offices in

Argentina Austria Brazil Chile Czech Republic France Greece
Guatemala Hungary Italy Japan Poland Portugal Singapore
South Korea Switzerland Thailand Turkey Ukraine Vietnam

OXFORD and OXFORD ENGLISH are registered trade marks of
Oxford University Press in the UK and in certain other countries

ACKNOWLEDGEMENTS

Illustrations by: Mark Duffin pp 10, 22, 34, 62, 64, 68; Geoff Waterhouse pp 13, 71

*We would also like to thank the following for permission to reproduce the following
photographs*: Cover images courtesy: RMI © Mango Productions/Corbis (girl at
screen), RMI © Simon Marcus (man in airport lounge), and Alex Mares-
Manton/Getty (girl in coffee bar), Alamy pp 26 (S.Frink Collection/dolphin), 32
(Image State), 52 (Image Source/Armand), 59 (F.Herholdt), 60 (D.Peebles
Photography); Anthony Blake Picture Library pp 9, 72 (G.Buntrock/bottle and
glass), 75 (Maximilian); Aviation-images.com pp 36, 38, 39; Cephas Picture
Library pp 65 (M.Rock), 72 (M.Rock/vineyard), 73 (B.Fleming); Corbis pp 26
(D.G.Houser/shops), 45 (L.Hebberd), 66; Getty Images pp 6 (A.Kuehn), 18
(Wides & Holl), 25 (B.Heinsohn), 28 (C.Sanders), 30 (D.Sacks/running
machines), 41 (M.Goldman), 48 (R.Daly/business meeting), (R.Lockyer/social
gathering), 49 (S.Watson), 52 (D.Lees/Maria), (S.Marks/Jason), 53 (S.Potter), 54
(J.Cooper), 56 (Chabruken), 70 (C.Ehlers); Getty News and Sport p 19
(P.Desmazes); Magnum Photos p 14 (© Stuart Franklin); Courtesy of Oxfam
pp 42, 44; Robert Harding Picture Library p 73; Royalty free pp 1, 15, 20, 23,
30 (woman pulling bar, step class), 55, 77; Still Pictures pp 12 (J.Boethling),
43 & 47 & 61 (all J.Schytte); Courtesy of Vinexpo p 8

*The authors and publisher are grateful to those who have given permission to reproduce
the following extracts and adaptations of copyright material*: p 44 'The Bangladeshi
success story' extract from www.oxfam.org.uk/what_we_do/fairtrade/
parables/incense/index.htm

Although every effort has been made to trace and contact copyright holders
before publication, this has not been possible in some cases. We apologize for
any apparent infringement of copyright and if notified, the publisher will be
pleased to rectify any errors or omissions at the earliest opportunity

Introduction

The twelve units in the Workbook give you extra practice of the language in the Student's Book. Each Workbook unit has four sections:

Language focus	has written exercises to practise the grammar in the Student's Book. There are drills for extra practice on the Student's CD.
Pronunciation	has listening and speaking exercises to give further pronunciation practice connected with the Student's Book.
Wordpower	practises the vocabulary in the Student's Book, and presents ways to learn and remember words.
Focus on functions	practises language for socializing with colleagues. All the conversations are on the CD. There are exercises to practise useful phrases from the conversations.

Study tips

- Use the CD with or without the Workbook, for example, in the car or on a personal stereo. Play the exercises and conversations as often as you like. Stop the CD and repeat useful words and phrases.

- Write your answers in the Workbook or write in a separate notebook. Use Workbook material for extra revision, for example, after Student's Book review units.

- Check your answers in the Answer key at the back of the Workbook. Refer to the Pocket Book for grammar explanations and useful social language.

- Use a good dictionary, for example, the *Oxford Wordpower Dictionary* and the *Oxford Dictionary of Business English* to help expand your vocabulary.

- Study every day if possible. You can work for a few minutes to complete an exercise then stop and do the next exercise later. The rule is, 'A little, but often.'

Contents

	Language focus	Pronunciation	Wordpower	Focus on functions
Unit 7 p.42	• Past Simple, Present Perfect Simple p.42	• Past Simple and Present Perfect Simple p.45	• The language of graphs p.46	• Opinions and suggestions p.47
Unit 8 p.48	• Modal auxiliary verbs p.48	• Sentence stress and emphasis p.51	• Word building p.51	• Invitations p.53
Unit 9 p.54	• Present Perfect Simple, Present Perfect Continuous p.54	• Word stress p.58	• Word families, collocations p.57	• Offers and requests p.59
Unit 10 p.60	• Future: *will*, 1st Conditional p.60	• *will* and *'ll* p.63	• Prepositions of place p.64	• Asking for information p.65
Unit 11 p.66	• 2nd Conditional p.66	• Contractions in 1st and 2nd Conditional sentences p.69	• Collocations, opposite adjectives p.70	• Social responses p.71
Unit 12 p.72	• Passive p.72	• Linking p.75	• Word building p.76	• Thanking for hospitality. Saying goodbye p.77

Listening scripts p.78
Answer key p.90

UNIT 1

Language focus **1 Present Simple positive**

Complete the Vinexpo exhibitor profile. Use the Present Simple form of the verbs in brackets.

EXHIBITOR PROFILE CARLA AND JASON LEONE-BELL	

VINEXPO

Carla and Jason _run_ ¹ (run) a very successful winemaking business. Carla _____² (come) from an old Italian family of winemakers in Cosenza and she _____³ (know) a lot about marketing wine. Jason _____⁴ (be) from the Barossa Valley, a famous wine region in south-east Australia. He _____⁵ (have) many years of winemaking experience with some of the Valley's great New World wines. Today, Carla and Jason _____⁶ (manage) their own big estate in the Puglia region of southern Italy. There, they _____⁷ (produce) their fine San Marco wine from the traditional primitivo grape. Thanks to Carla's hard work, wine experts all over the world _____⁸ (know) the San Marco name. Jason says, 'I _____⁹ (help) with new ideas on wine production, and Carla _____¹⁰ (persuade) the customers to buy our product.'

Come and meet Carla and Jason on Stand 206 – and try the product!

2 Present Simple positive and negative

Complete the sentences about Carla and Jason using the Vinexpo exhibitor profile in **1** and the business cards. Use the Present Simple form of the verbs in brackets.

SAN MARCO SpA	**SAN MARCO SpA**
Jason Bell Director, Wine Production Via Della Viole San Marco in Lámis Puglia 73041 Tel: (+0039) 0883 937756 Email: jbell@smarco.it	**Carla Leone-Bell** Marketing Director Via Della Viole San Marco in Lámis Puglia 73041 Tel: (+0039) 0883 937757 Email: cleonebell@smarco.it

1 Jason _comes_ (come) from a wine-growing area of Australia.

2 His wife, Carla, _doesn't come_ (come) from Australia.

3 Carla _____ (be) from an old Italian family of winemakers.

4 Jason _____ (live) in Australia now.

5 Jason and Carla _____ (live) near San Marco in Puglia, southern Italy.

6 They _____ (work) on Carla's family estate.

7 They _____ (produce) very good wine on their own estate.

8 Jason _____ (run) the production side of the business.

9 He _____ (help) with new ideas on marketing.

10 Carla _____ (manage) the marketing for the business.

❸ Present Simple *Yes / No* questions

Complete the conversation between Helen and Rosa, two visitors at Vinexpo. Use the Present Simple form of the verbs in brackets.

HELEN	Oh, no! I can't find my programme. <u>*Do you have*</u> [1] (you / have) a programme Rosa?
ROSA	Yes, I do. _____ [2] (you / want) to borrow it?
HELEN	No, but could you check the time of the talk on biotechnology and wine-growing? _____ [3] (it / start) at 11.00 or at 11.30?
ROSA	Let's see ... It begins at 11.00.
HELEN	And _____ [4] (it / finish) at 1.00? I have a meeting at lunchtime.
ROSA	Yes, it does. It looks very interesting.
HELEN	I agree. _____ [5] (you / be) interested in going, too?
ROSA	Yes, I am. But _____ [6] (I / need) a ticket?
HELEN	No, you don't. We can go together.
ROSA	Fine, but _____ [7] (we / have) time to go to the cafeteria first? I really need a coffee before I think about wine!

❹ Present Simple *Wh-* questions

Complete the publicity material about Vinexpo. Use the question words in the box.

> How many   ~~What~~   What   When   Where   Who   Why

FACTS

VINEXPO

<u>*What*</u> [1] **is Vinexpo?**
Vinexpo is an international exhibition for the wine and spirits business.

_____ [2] **does it take place?**
The main exhibition is in Bordeaux, but there are also shows in the Far East and America.

_____ [3] **does the main exhibition take place?**
In June, every two years.

_____ [4] **is Vinexpo for?**
Producers, distributors, and retailers from all over the world.

_____ [5] **exhibitors come to Bordeaux?**
About 2,500, and they come from more than 40 countries.

_____ [6] **do they come back year after year?**
Because Vinexpo is the top international wine fair and a great place to do business.

_____ [7] **date is the next Vinexpo?**
From 22 to 26 June. Put it in your diary now!

❺ Present Simple questions

Complete the conversation between Carla and Peter Stephanopoulos. Use the words in brackets to write the questions.

PETER   Hello. _Are you Signora Leone-Bell_ ¹?

               (Leone-Bell / Signora / you / are)

CARLA   That's right. Carla Leone-Bell.

PETER   Nice to meet you. I'm Peter Stephanopoulos, from Australia.

CARLA   Nice to meet you, too. _____ ²?

               (from / are / Sydney / you)

PETER   Yes, I am. _____ ³?

               (from / which / of / you / are / part / Italy)

CARLA   I'm from the south. _____ ⁴?

               (do / do / you / what)

PETER   I'm a wine importer. Here's my card.

CARLA   So, _____ ⁵?

               (do / import / you / wine / Italian)

PETER   No, not at the moment.

CARLA   That's terrible! Here's a San Marco 2003.

               _____ ⁶?

               (you / do / want / to / it / taste)

PETER   Yes, please. Mmm, it's excellent.

               _____ ⁷?

               (you / do / what / use / grape)

CARLA   Primitivo. It's the traditional grape in our part of Italy.

PETER   But there's something Australian about this wine.

CARLA   Yes, have a look at this business card.

               _____ ⁸?

               (name / the / you / know / do)

PETER   Jason Bell? The Australian winemaker?

               _____ ⁹?

               (he / your / is / husband)

CARLA   Yes, and this is his wine!

❻ Frequency adverbs

How often do you eat out? Tick (✓) your answers on the questionnaire.

Eating out

1 How often do you eat out at a restaurant?

a) nearly every day	☐	d) once or twice a month	☐
b) once or twice a week	☐	e) a few times a year	☐
c) 3 or 4 times a week	☐	f) never	☐

2 What sort of food do you like?

a) Indian	☐	d) Chinese	☐
b) French	☐	e) Other...............................	
c) Italian	☐	(PLEASE WRITE WHAT SORT)	

3 When do you eat out at a restaurant?

	NEVER	SOMETIMES	OFTEN	ALWAYS
a) when you meet friends	☐	☐	☐	☐
b) on business	☐	☐	☐	☐
c) on special occasions, for example, birthdays	☐	☐	☐	☐
d) when you're tired and don't want to cook	☐	☐	☐	☐

Read about Peter Stephanopoulos. Then complete the paragraph below about you in a similar way.

> Peter Stephanopoulos eats out at a restaurant once or twice a week. He likes Greek, Italian, and Chinese food. He often eats at a restaurant on business. He sometimes eats at a restaurant on special occasions, for example, birthdays.

I eat out at a restaurant ... _____

_____

_____

_____

❼ Practice drills: Present Simple

🎧 **1.1, 1.2** Follow the instructions on the Student's CD/Cassette. If necessary, refer to the Listening scripts on p.78.

 Pocket Book p. 12

Pronunciation   Intonation of questions

Read the questions aloud. Do they rise ↗ or fall ↘ ?
Mark the intonation.

1	Who is Vinexpo for?	↘
2	Does it finish at 1.00?	↗
3	Are you interested in going?	____
4	What do you do?	____
5	How many exhibitors come?	____
6	Do you use English at work?	____
7	Are you from Sydney?	____
8	What date is the next Vinexpo?	____
9	Which part of Italy are you from?	____
10	Do you import Italian wine?	____

🎧 **1.3** Listen and repeat the questions.

---

① Personal information

Write the headings for the hotel guest registration card. Use the words and phrases in the box.

> Country of residence   Home address   Passport no.   Signature
> Date of birth   Mobile   Place of birth   ~~Surname~~
> Email address   Nationality   Post code   Telephone
> Forename(s)

PRINCES HOTEL
GUEST REGISTRATION CARD

Surname	1	Watts
	2	Paul John
	3	4 Forest Road, London
	4	SW3 5NT
	5	0208 73921
	6	07974201223
	7	paulwatts@gkmail.com
	8	15/04/75
	9	Manchester

(FOR OVERSEAS VISITORS ONLY)

	10	British
	11	C610392D
	12	UK
	13	P J Watts

② Personal possessions

Look at the picture. Complete the list of things in the briefcase.

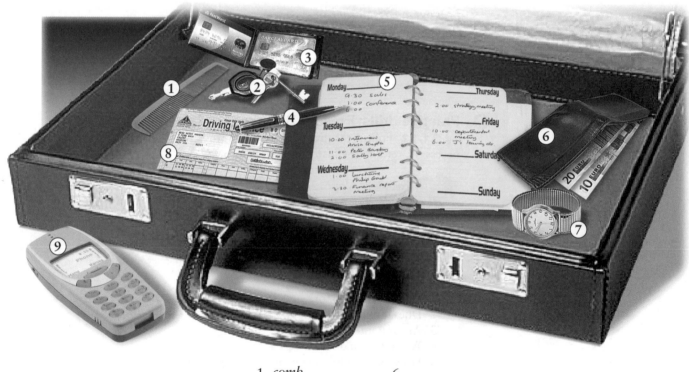

1 *comb*	6 _____	_____
2 _____	7 _____	_____
3 _____	8 _____	_____
4 _____	9 _____	_____
5 _____	_____	_____

What other personal possessions do you usually carry? Add them to the list.

Introductions, greetings, and goodbyes

Complete the four conversations. Use the phrases in the box.

How's life?	May I introduce myself?
Good to see you again.	let me introduce you
Pleased to meet you.	I look forward to seeing you in Madrid.
it was very nice meeting you.	How do you do?

Conversation 1

CHARLES   David, _____ [1] to
        Kristal Schwartz. Kristal, this is David Porter. David, this is
        Kristal Schwartz.

KRISTAL   Hello. _____ [2]

DAVID   Pleased to meet you, too.

Conversation 2

MR WEST   Excuse me, but are you Mrs Rice?

MRS RICE   Yes, that's right.

MR WEST   _____ [3] I'm Michael West.

MRS RICE   How do you do?

MR WEST   _____ [4]

Conversation 3

ALAN   Hello, Lucy. How are you?

LUCY   Fine, thanks, Alan. _____ [5]

ALAN   Nice to see you, too. How's the family?

LUCY   They're all very well. _____ [6]

ALAN   Oh, not too bad, thanks, but very busy.

Conversation 4

BARBARA   Patrick, I must go now – my flight is at 5.00.

PATRICK   Well, _____ [7]

BARBARA   I really enjoyed meeting you, too.

PATRICK   _____ [8]

BARBARA   I do, too. See you next month.

🎧 **1.4** Listen to the conversations and check your answers.

🎧 **1.5** Listen and repeat the phrases on the Student's CD/Cassette.

📕 **Pocket Book p. 18**

UNIT 2

1 **Present Simple**

Complete the magazine article. Use the Present Simple form of the verbs in brackets.

INDIA'S HIGH-TECH CITY

going global

On busy Mahatma Gandhi Road, hundreds of small shops _sell_____[1] (sell) everything from gold to hot food. Business _____[2] (take) place from morning until night. It _____[3] (seem) like a normal Indian city street – but all the roofs _____[4] (have) satellite dishes. Mahatma Gandhi Road, in the clean, green city of Bangalore, is the centre of India's new software industry.

Indian software engineers are very good, and they also _____[5] (speak) good English. Large organizations like IBM and Siemens _____[6] (want) their skills.

The German company Siemens, based in Munich, _____[7] (employ) hundreds of engineers in Bangalore as troubleshooters*, and the system _____[8] (work) like this. When the Munich engineers _____[9] (find) a problem, they _____[10] (send) the data at the end of their day. The Indian section _____[11] (deal) with the problem and then _____[12] (return) the data – before next morning in Germany!

troubleshooter: a person who deals with problems in a company/organization

2 **Present Continuous: spelling**

Write the Present Continuous form of the verbs in the box in the correct column.

become	get	reduce	stop	try
cut	grow	start	take	use
forget	handle	stay	travel	work

answer-**ing**	arriv(**e**)-**ing**	begin-**n-ing**
growing	_becoming_	_cutting_
_____	_____	_____
_____	_____	_____
_____	_____	_____
_____	_____	_____

❸ Present Continuous positive

Complete the sentences. Use the Present Continuous form of the verbs in brackets.

1 The world *is becoming* _____ (become) a very small place.

2 Business people _____ (travel) to lots of different countries.

3 The Internet _____ (reduce) the cost of communication.

4 International phone calls _____ (get) cheaper.

5 Business _____ (begin) to work in new ways.

6 E-commerce _____ (grow) very quickly.

7 Some US companies _____ (handle) their paperwork overnight in Ireland.

8 Some UK companies _____ (answer) customer inquiries through call centres in India.

9 Many organizations _____ (try) to reduce their costs.

10 Employees _____ (work) from their computers at home.

❹ Present Continuous positive and negative

DfComp is a computer company on Mahatma Ghandi Road. Write sentences about the company's current activities. Use the words in brackets and the Present Continuous form.

1 *The company is expanding its activities in India.* _____

(the company / expand / its activities in India)

2 _____

(the company / not employ / new staff in the Bangalore office)

3 _____

(they / open / new offices in Chennai and Mumbai)

4 _____

(the company / not plan / to expand overseas at the present time)

5 _____

(sales of the company's home computers / increasing)

6 _____

(they / not make / changes to their software programs)

7 _____

(the Managing Director / have / a lot of meetings with IBM)

⑤ Present Continuous questions

Sue MacDonald is telephoning her business partner, Ian Taylor. Complete the conversation. Use the Present Continuous form of the verbs in the box.

> do   ~~enjoy~~   tell   work
> do   phone   visit

SUE   Ian? It's Sue here. Good afternoon from Spain.

IAN   Hello, Sue! *Are you enjoying* [1] your trip?

SUE   Yes, I am. Miguel is introducing me to a lot of new contacts.

IAN   Ah, Miguel, your new agent! _____ [2] a good job?

SUE   Yes, an excellent job.

IAN   So, where _____ [3] from?

SUE   I'm in Seville.

IAN   Seville? Who _____ [4] in Seville?

SUE   Miguel knows an important olive oil supplier here.

IAN   So, what _____ [5] right now?

SUE   I'm with the Sales Director of the olive oil company.

IAN   _____ [6] him about the demand for good olive oil in the UK?

SUE   Yes, I am, and I need the latest sales figures for our discussion. _____ [7] on them at the moment?

IAN   Yes, I'm printing them now – and they're good!

SUE   That's great! Could you fax them to me?

IAN   Sure.

❻ Present Simple and Present Continuous

Complete the text. Use the Present Simple or Present Continuous form of the verbs in brackets.

Ian Taylor and Sue MacDonald _live_____¹ (live) in London, and they _____² (run) a small company that _____³ (import) fine food. After a slow start two years ago, their company _____⁴ (grow) fast now. Sales _____⁵ (rise) and they _____⁶ (try) to increase their range of products. Sue usually _____⁷ (deal) with this part of the business. Her agent in Spain, Miguel Sanchez, _____⁸ (look) for new suppliers for her at the moment. This week, Sue _____⁹ (visit) some of them with Miguel. Today, they _____¹⁰ (have) a meeting with an olive oil supplier in Seville.

❼ Practice drills: Present Continuous

 2.1, 2.2 Follow the instructions on the Student's CD/Cassette. If necessary, refer to the Listening scripts on p.79.

> Pocket Book p. 11

Pronunciation Strong and weak forms of _do_ and _does_

Read the sentences aloud. Is the pronunciation of _do_ strong or weak? Tick (✓) the correct column.

	a (strong)	b (weak)
1 Do you know the place?	_____	✓
2 Yes, I do.	✓	_____
3 Where does he work?	_____	_____
4 Does he work in Paris?	_____	_____
5 Yes, he does.	_____	_____
6 When do they leave?	_____	_____
7 Do they often fly?	_____	_____
8 Yes, they do.	_____	_____

 2.3 Listen and repeat the sentences.

Verb groups

❶ Write *do*, *have*, *make*, and *work* in the correct group below.

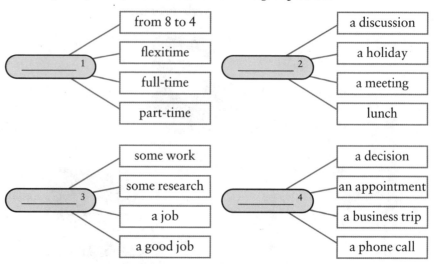

from 8 to 4

flexitime

full-time

part-time

a discussion

a holiday

a meeting

lunch

some work

some research

a job

a good job

a decision

an appointment

a business trip

a phone call

❷ Complete the sentences. Use the phrases from the verb groups in **❶**.

1 A: Could I *make an appointment* _____ to discuss the sales figures?

B: Of course. Is Friday at two OK?

2 As usual, your work is very good. You always _____ .

3 A: What are your hours?

B: I _____ – two days a week.

4 We _____ here. You can start at 8.30, 9.00 or 9.30.

5 It's 12.30. Let's go to the pizzeria and _____ .

6 Could I use your mobile? I need to _____ .

7 A: I want to find information about the market in France.

B: Why don't you _____ on the Internet?

8 I usually _____ in September when the weather is good.

❸ Complete the word map. Use the words and phrases in the box.

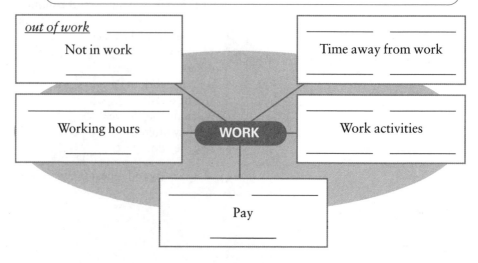

emails	meetings	reports	unemployed
flexitime	~~out of work~~	retired	wages
full-time	part-time	salary	
holidays	paternity leave	sick leave	
maternity leave	phone calls	sick pay	

out of work _____

Not in work

_____

_____ _____

Time away from work

_____

_____ _____

Working hours

_____

WORK

_____ _____

Work activities

_____

_____ _____

Pay

_____

Making contact

Complete the telephone conversation. Use the phrases in the box.

> Could you ask her to call me
> I'm sorry, she's away today.
> Can you spell that, please?
> Who's calling, please?
> Hold the line, please.
>
> Can I speak to
> can I have your number?
> Could you give her a message?
> Could you tell me your name again

RECEPTIONIST Good afternoon. Global Travel. How can I help you?

CALLER Hello. _____ [1] Emma Norton, please?

RECEPTIONIST _____ [2]

CALLER It's George Kolasinski.

RECEPTIONIST Thank you. _____ [3] I'll put you through to her office.

CALLER Thank you.

COLLEAGUE Emma Norton's phone. David Lawson here. Can I help you?

CALLER Oh, this is George Kolasinski. Could I speak to Emma, please?

COLLEAGUE _____ [4]

CALLER Oh, no! I need to speak to her – it's quite important.

COLLEAGUE Perhaps I can help you.

CALLER Thank you. _____ [5]

COLLEAGUE Yes, of course.

CALLER _____ [6] tomorrow morning?

COLLEAGUE Yes, certainly. _____ [7], please?

CALLER It's Kolasinski. George Kolasinski.

COLLEAGUE _____ [8]

CALLER It's K-O-L-A-S-I-N-S-K-I.

COLLEAGUE And _____ [9]

CALLER It's 0-1-6-5-7, 3-double two-5-8-9-0.

COLLEAGUE Right. So that's Mr George Kolasinski on 0-1-6-5-7, 3-double two-5-8-9-0.

CALLER That's it. Thanks very much. Goodbye.

COLLEAGUE Goodbye.

🎧 **2.4** Listen to the conversation and check your answers.

🎧 **2.5** Listen and repeat the phrases on the Student's CD/Cassette.

◆ **Pocket Book p. 22**

TELEPHONE MESSAGE PAD

To: Emma Norton   From: David Lawson
Date: 15 October   Time: 3.45

While you were out

Mr George Kolasinski

of:

Phone No. 01657 3225890

☑ Telephoned   ☑ Please call
☐ Was in to see you ☐ Will call back
☐ Wants to see you   ☑ URGENT
☐ Returned your call

Message: Call tomorrow morning

UNIT 3

1 **Past Simple regular verbs**

Complete the interview with an international photographer. Use the Past Simple form of the verbs in brackets.

INTERVIEWER Anne-Marie Colville is a photographer, and she travels all over the world. Anne-Marie, tell us about your work.

ANNE-MARIE Well, you're right, I travel a lot. Last month, for example, I _worked_ [1] (work) in three different parts of Africa.

INTERVIEWER Which places _____ you _____ [2] (visit)?

ANNE-MARIE I _____ [3] (start) in Cape Town. My agency _____ [4] (need) some pictures of a big, international meeting.

INTERVIEWER How long _____ you _____ [5] (stay) there?

ANNE-MARIE Five days.

INTERVIEWER _____ you _____ [6] (return) to Paris?

ANNE-MARIE Well, I _____ [7] (arrive) at the airport, but then the agency _____ [8] (call) me. They _____ [9] (want) pictures of a national park in Kenya.

INTERVIEWER _____ you _____ [10] (agree) to go?

ANNE-MARIE Sure. I just _____ [11] (change) my flight. It was a nice job. The pictures were good too.

INTERVIEWER So what then?

ANNE-MARIE Then the agency _____ [12] (suggest) another African job. That was a trip to Addis Ababa for some pictures of the great Ethiopian runner, Haile Gebrselassie.

❷ Past Simple regular and irregular verbs

Complete the magazine article. Use the Past Simple form of the verbs in brackets.

HAILE GEBRSELASSIE: A MAN WITH TWO CHALLENGES

Haile _grew_ [1] (grow) up on a small farm in the mountains of Ethiopia. The long run to school every day _____ [2] (help) to make him the world's best distance runner. At sixteen years old, he _____ [3] (run) his first important marathon. At seventeen, he _____ [4] (go) to live with his older brother in the capital, Addis Ababa. There, he _____ [5] (begin) training full-time.

A few months later, in 1991, Ethiopia _____ [6] (choose) Haile to run for his country. The next year, he _____ [7] (become) the world junior champion at 5,000 and 10,000 metres. The year after that, he _____ [8] (win) again – as a senior. That _____ [9] (make) him a national hero and an international superstar.

During the 1990s, he _____ [10] (break) many records – mostly his own! In 2003, at the age of twenty-nine, he still _____ [11] (have) the power to break the two-mile world record.

Early in the 1990s, Haile _____ [12] (accept) a very different challenge. Ethiopia is a poor country, with a lot of unemployment. Haile _____ [13] (decide) to use money from his running to help his country. He _____ [14] (open) a café and a construction company with his brothers. These businesses _____ [15] (create) jobs for 300 people. He was very happy and very proud.

❸ Past time expressions

Give true answers to these questions. Use the time expressions in the box.

> Last night / week / weekend / month   On Monday / Tuesday …
> The day / night / week before last   Yesterday

1 When did you last do some exercise?
   Yesterday. I played a game of tennis. / The night before last. I went
   running for an hour. / Last weekend. I did some training at the gym.

2 When did you last have a holiday?
   _____

3 When did you last see a good film at the cinema?
   _____

4 When did you last go to a concert?
   _____

5 When did you last listen to the radio?
   _____

6 When did you last read a good book?
   _____

④ Past Simple questions

A television presenter interviewed two businesspeople. Use the words in brackets to write the questions.

LUCY   Welcome to *Business Challenge*. I'm Lucy Long, and tonight I'm asking some entrepreneurs how they began. Sita Gupta, tell us about your Internet cafés. <u>*Did you start SG Intercafés alone?*</u>   ¹?
(alone / SG Intercafés / you / start / did)

SITA   No, I had some technical help with the computers from my brother, Ranjit.

LUCY   _____ ²?
(big / there / any / were / problems)

SITA   Well, money was a big problem.

LUCY   _____ ³?
(the / did / bank / much / help)

SITA   No, it didn't help much in the first year. It was a really difficult time.

LUCY   _____ ⁴?
(fast / grow / that / after / business / the / did)

SITA   Yes, it did. I opened two more Internet cafés in London in the second year, and we now have cafés in several cities in Europe.

LUCY   And now Bill Sullivan, head of Forest Housing.

_____ ⁵?
(company / did / start / your / you / when)

BILL   About five years ago.

LUCY   _____ ⁶?
(you / it / why / Housing / call / Forest / did)

BILL   I chose the name because our houses are made of wood from the forests of Sweden. They're a Swedish design.

LUCY   Sita's big problem in her first year was money.

_____ ⁷?
(problems / have / what / you / did)

BILL   One big problem was people. It was very hard to find the right people with the right skills.

❺ Past Simple questions

One of Bill Sullivan's problems was his first agent in Sweden, Ted Ross. Read Ted's email to Bill. Then complete Bill's reply. Use the question words to write the questions.

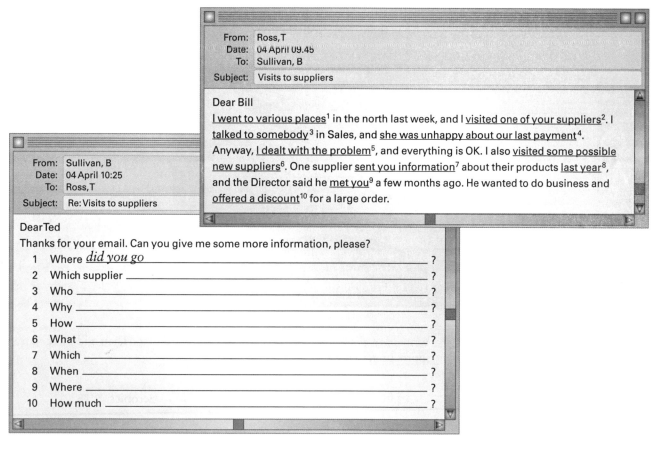

From: Ross, T
Date: 04 April 09.45
To: Sullivan, B
Subject: Visits to suppliers

Dear Bill
I went to various places[1] in the north last week, and I visited one of your suppliers[2]. I talked to somebody[3] in Sales, and she was unhappy about our last payment[4]. Anyway, I dealt with the problem[5], and everything is OK. I also visited some possible new suppliers[6]. One supplier sent you information[7] about their products last year[8], and the Director said he met you[9] a few months ago. He wanted to do business and offered a discount[10] for a large order.

From: Sullivan, B
Date: 04 April 10:25
To: Ross, T
Subject: Re: Visits to suppliers

Dear Ted
Thanks for your email. Can you give me some more information, please?

1 Where *did you go* _____ ?
2 Which supplier _____ ?
3 Who _____ ?
4 Why _____ ?
5 How _____ ?
6 What _____ ?
7 Which _____ ?
8 When _____ ?
9 Where _____ ?
10 How much _____ ?

❻ Practice drills: Past Simple

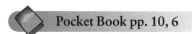 **3.1, 3.2** Follow the instructions on the Student's CD/Cassette. If necessary, refer to the Listening scripts on p.80.

Pocket Book pp. 10, 6

Pronunciation -ed endings in the Past Simple

Read the verbs aloud and tick (✓) the correct column.

	/d/	/t/	/ɪd/
1 asked		✓	
2 complained	✓		
3 decided			✓
4 faxed			
5 lasted			
6 picked			
7 played			
8 reported			
9 returned			
10 stopped			
11 travelled			
12 visited			

3.3 Listen and repeat the verbs.

Sports and leisure

1 Look at the leaflet. Write the words and phrases in the box next to the correct picture.

aerobics	fitness training	squash	tennis
badminton	judo	~~swimming~~	weight training
basketball	rollerblading	table tennis	yoga

2 Write *play*, *do*, and *go* in the centre of each word map. Then add three more sports or activities.

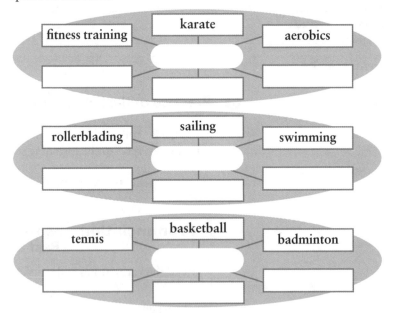

3 Complete the leaflet extract. Rearrange the words in brackets.

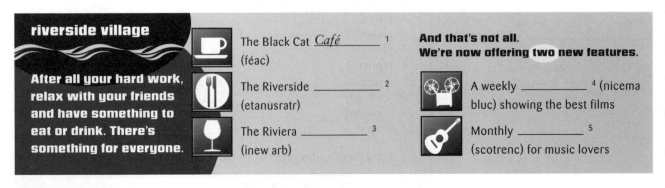

riverside village

After all your hard work, relax with your friends and have something to eat or drink. There's something for everyone.

The Black Cat *Café* 1 (féac)

The Riverside _____ 2 (etanusratr)

The Riviera _____ 3 (inew arb)

And that's not all.
We're now offering two new features.

A weekly _____ 4 (nicema bluc) showing the best films

Monthly _____ 5 (scotrenc) for music lovers

Welcoming a visitor

Takashi Miura, a fashion buyer from Tokyo, is visiting Paola Silvestrini at her company in Milan. Complete the conversation. Use the phrases in the box.

> What was the weather like   how did you get here?
> Did you have any problems finding us?   Is this your first visit
> How was your stay   Did you have a good journey?

PAOLA   Good to see you again, Takashi, and welcome to Italy.

TAKASHI   Thank you, Paola. It's nice to be here.

PAOLA   _____ [1] to this part of Italy?

TAKASHI   Yes, it is. I only know Rome.

PAOLA   So ... _____ [2]

TAKASHI   Well, I flew to Rome on Saturday and stayed two nights there. Then I took the train from Rome to Milan this morning.

PAOLA   _____ [3]

TAKASHI   Yes, thanks. The train was very comfortable.

PAOLA   _____ [4]

TAKASHI   No, none at all. Your directions were fine.

PAOLA   _____ [5] in Rome?

TAKASHI   Very pleasant, thanks. I did some sightseeing and some shopping, of course.

PAOLA   Good. And I'm pleased you're seeing Milan in the sun. Spring has come early this year. _____ [6] in Tokyo when you left?

TAKASHI   Well, actually, it was very wet there. So I came to Milan at the right time!

🎧 **3.4** Listen to the conversation and check your answers.

🎧 **3.5** Listen and repeat the questions on the Student's CD/Cassette.

◆ **Pocket Book p. 23**

UNIT 4

Language focus **1** **Future: Present Continuous**

BioPharma International has intercultural communication problems. Personnel Director Petra Schuman wants Global Training's help and is arranging a meeting with Mark Grady. Read their diaries and complete the conversation. Use the Present Continuous form of the verbs in the box.

(not) do	give	make	write
~~fly~~	interview	meet	

PETRA SCHUMAN

Wed	a.m.–President at HQ
Thurs	2.30–5.30 interviews: job applicants
Fri	p.m.–reports

MARK GRADY

WED	1.00 – to Paris
THURS	a.m.–presentation (AG Bank, London)
FRI	p.m.– training video
SAT	

PETRA   Listen, Mark, are you free on Wednesday?

MARK   Well, I *'m flying* _____ [1] to Paris at 1.00 for an afternoon meeting. How about Wednesday morning?

PETRA   No, I can't manage the morning. I _____ [2] the President at our headquarters. Are you back from Paris on Thursday morning?

MARK   Yes, but I _____ [3] a presentation here in London then. What about the afternoon?

PETRA   No, that's no good for me. I _____ [4] job applicants all afternoon. How about Friday? I _____ [5] reports in the afternoon ...

MARK   I'm busy then, too. I _____ [6] a training video in the afternoon. But I _____ [7] anything in the morning.

PETRA   Great. I'm free then, too.

2 **Future: Present Continuous questions**

BioPharma's President, Jay Walker, is asking about a seminar that Petra is organizing. Complete his questions. Use the Present Continuous form of the verbs in brackets.

1 Where *are we holding* _____ (we / hold) the seminar?

2 _____ (you / invite) only division managers?

3 When _____ (it / take) place?

4 How many _____ (people / go) to the seminar?

5 _____ (you / lead) the seminar alone?

6 When _____ (I / talk) to everyone – at the start or at the end?

❸ Future: Present Continuous answers

Use the information from Petra's fax below to write her answers to the President's questions on p. 24. Use the Present Continuous form.

04 02/23 MÅN 13.51 FAX 031 316b368   BIOPHARMA INT AB   001

BioPharma International   Fax

To: All Division Managers Date: 12 May
           (US and European Operations)
           All training staff

From: P Schuman
           Personnel Director (European Division)

Subject: Seminar on 'Intercultural Communication – the way forward for BioPharma' 2–4 June, at the Cape Coral Hotel, Nassau, Bahamas Islands

Staff attending: All division managers and all training staff (Total 97)

Seminar leaders: P Schuman, Mark Grady (of Global Training)

Please arrange to arrive in Nassau by late afternoon, 1 June. Welcome drinks in the hotel bar from 7.30, followed by dinner.

Schedule:
Friday 2 June
7.30–8.00   Breakfast
9.00–9.45   Keynote talk by Company President Jay Walker: 'Communicate – or Die!'

1 *We're holding the seminar at the Cape Coral Hotel in Nassau.*

2 _____

3 _____

4 _____

5 _____

6 _____

4 **Future:** *going to*

Read the tourist information about the Bahamas Islands. Complete the statements. Write what the visitors are going to do.

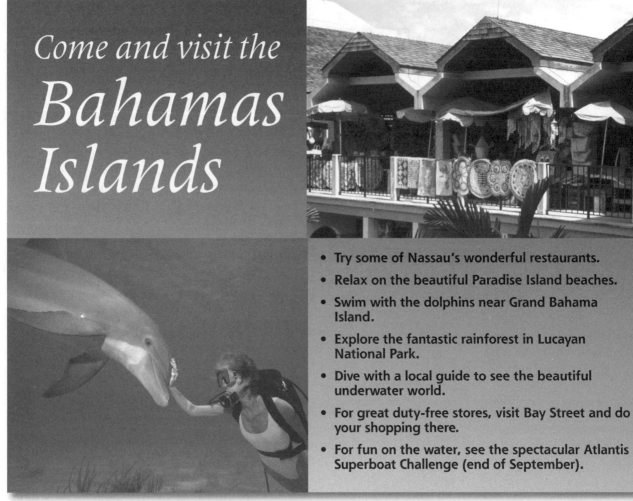

Come and visit the
Bahamas Islands

- Try some of Nassau's wonderful restaurants.
- Relax on the beautiful Paradise Island beaches.
- Swim with the dolphins near Grand Bahama Island.
- Explore the fantastic rainforest in Lucayan National Park.
- Dive with a local guide to see the beautiful underwater world.
- For great duty-free stores, visit Bay Street and do your shopping there.
- For fun on the water, see the spectacular Atlantis Superboat Challenge (end of September).

1 I want to buy some presents. *I'm going to visit Bay Street and do my shopping there.*

2 We don't want to eat at the hotel all the time. *We* _____

_____

3 My daughter loves dolphins. _____

_____

4 My sister and her family just want a quiet holiday with sand, sea, and sun.

_____

5 I love speedboats, and I'm planning to visit the Bahamas in the last week of September. _____

_____

6 My brother wants to try taking photos underwater. _____

_____

7 We don't want to spend all our time in Nassau, or on the beach, or in the sea. _____

_____

❺ Future: *going to* questions

Rosa Sanchez wants to open a restaurant in Nassau. A journalist is asking about her plans. Complete the journalist's questions. Use *going to* with the words in brackets.

1 When <u>*are you going to open*</u> (you / open) your new restaurant?

2 _____ (it / be) in the middle of town?

3 What kind of menu _____ (you / offer)?

4 How _____ (you / compete) with all the other fish restaurants?

5 How many _____ (people / work) in the restaurant?

6 When _____ (the builders / start) work?

7 How long _____ (the building work / take)?

8 How much _____ (the whole project / cost)?

Now match the journalist's questions to Rosa's answers.

a Between eight and nine months, I think.   <u>7</u>

b About 120,000 US dollars.   _____

c No, it's going to be by the old harbour.   _____

d As soon as the planners agree to the building plans.   _____

e Oh, we're going to specialize in seafood.   _____

f I hope we're going to be ready for business by the end of this year.   _____

g I expect to start with about ten staff.   _____

h That's easy! We're going to provide a really wonderful eating experience!   _____

❻ Practice drills: *going to*

🎧 **4.1, 4.2** Follow the instructions on the Student's CD/Cassette. If necessary, refer to the Listening scripts on p.81.

Pocket Book p. 4

Pronunciation   Word stress: countries and nationalities

Mark the stressed syllables.

A·merica	A·merican	Germany	German
Ja·pan	Japa·nese	Hungary	Hungarian
Australia	Australian	India	Indian
Belgium	Belgian	Italy	Italian
Canada	Canadian	Kuwait	Kuwaiti
China	Chinese	Pakistan	Pakistani
Egypt	Egyptian	Poland	Polish
Europe	European	Portugal	Portuguese

🎧 **4.3** Listen and repeat the countries and nationalities.

Hotels

❶ Complete the conversations. Use the pairs of words and phrases in the box.

> bath / shower   ~~double room / twin room~~   suitcase / luggage
> bill / receipt   half-board / full-board

1 A So, Ms Tate, you'd like a room for two. Would you like a
   double room ?
   B No. I'm coming with my sister, so we'd like a _twin room_ ,
   please.

2 A Would you like _____ ?
   B No, thanks. We plan to go out for lunch, so we'd just like
   _____ , please.

3 A Would you like some help with your _____ , sir?
   B No thanks. I've only got one _____ .

4 A The bathroom's very small. It's only got a _____ !
   B I'm sorry, madam. I'll see if I have a room with a full bathroom,
   including a _____ .

5 A Would you like anything else? More coffee, perhaps?
   B No, thanks. Could I just have the _____ ?
   Oh, and I'll need a _____ , please.

❷ Complete the information about the Cape Coral Hotel. Use the words and phrases in the box.

> business centre   fitness centre   safe
> cocktail bar   ~~multi-line phone~~   satellite TV
> computer / fax point   minibar   swimming-pool
> conference facilities   restaurants   24-hour room service

The *Cape Coral Hotel* welcomes you to the '*Best of the Bahamas*'

Personal in-room facilities

multi-line phone ¹ Call direct locally or internationally.

_____ ² Send and receive all your emails and other written communications.

_____ ³ Choose from 220 channels in five languages.

_____ ⁴ Keep passports, money, and other valuables in here.

_____ ⁵ Choose from a selection of soft and alcoholic drinks.

_____ ⁶ Order a snack or a full meal at any time of day or night. Just dial 111.

Facilities for all our guests

Business: Use our superbly equipped _____ ⁷, complete with office and secretarial facilities. Cape Coral is also a wonderful place for business meetings of any size. We offer first-class _____ ⁸, with rooms that hold from 30 to 300 people.

Sports and leisure: Work out on the wide range of machines in our _____ ⁹. Or use our spectacular outdoor _____ ¹⁰. Swim, or just relax and sunbathe.

Eating and social: Meet friends and colleagues for a social drink in the Coral Beach _____ ¹¹. Then choose from our four excellent _____ ¹² for lunch or dinner. The cuisine at Cape Coral is famous!

Staying at a hotel

Complete the three conversations. Use the phrases in the box.

> Could I have an early-morning call?   Can I pay by credit card?
> Good. I'll pay by Mastercard then.   I'd like to book a single room.
> For one night.   Could I have my bill, please?
> For Wednesday the 16th of June.   I have a reservation.

Conversation 1

RECEPTIONIST Cape Coral Hotel. Good morning. How may I help you?

CALLER Oh, hello. _____ 1

RECEPTIONIST Yes, certainly, madam. When is that for?

CALLER _____ 2

RECEPTIONIST And for how many nights?

CALLER _____ 3

RECEPTIONIST OK. And could I have your name, please?

CALLER Yes, it's Paola Giacalone.

RECEPTIONIST Fine. I'll reserve a room for you immediately.

Conversation 2

GUEST Hello. My name's Paola Giacalone.

_____ 4

RECEPTIONIST Oh, yes. Good evening, madam. Welcome to the Cape Coral Hotel. Could you fill in this form, please?

GUEST Sure.

RECEPTIONIST Can you sign here, please? ... Thank you. Here's your keycard.

GUEST Thanks. _____ 5

RECEPTIONIST Yes, of course. At what time?

GUEST At 6.45, please.

Conversation 3

GUEST Good morning. _____ 6

RECEPTIONIST Certainly, madam. Did you have anything from the minibar last night?

GUEST No, nothing.

RECEPTIONIST Fine. Here's your bill.

GUEST Thank you.

RECEPTIONIST How would you like to pay?

GUEST _____ 7

RECEPTIONIST Yes, that's fine.

GUEST _____ 8

🎧 **4.4** Listen to the conversations and check your answers.

🎧 **4.5** Listen and repeat the phrases on the Student's CD/Cassette.

◆ **Pocket Book p. 22**

UNIT 5

1 Mass and count nouns

Read the leaflet. Underline the correct alternative.

Lifestyle FITNESS STUDIO

Everybody wants *good health* / *a good health* [1]. At **LIFESTYLE** we help you to get fit and stay fit. We offer *regular training* / *a regular training* [2] with a personalized fitness programme.

Our new fitness studio has all the fitness *machine* / *machines* [3] and other *equipment* / *equipments* [4] you need. Personal trainers, Jill and Nick, are there to give *advice* / *advices* [5].

In today's busy world, people don't have a lot of *time* / *times* [6] for exercise. *Research* / *Researches* [7] suggests that 'little and often' is good for you. So try to visit us three times a week. You'll soon start to see positive *result* / *results* [8].

And it isn't all *hard work* / *a hard work* [9]. After your workout, stop at our Lifestyle Restaurant and enjoy a healthy meal. *A relaxation* / *Relaxation* [10] is good for you too!

For more *information* / *informations* [11]
call us on 01367 712399.

2 Mass and count nouns: general and specific meaning

Complete the pairs of sentences. Use the singular or plural form of the nouns in the box.

> business   food   life   sport
> exercise   fruit   noise   ~~time~~

1 a Tony goes to Lifestyle fitness studio four _times_____ a week.

   b It takes _time_____ to get fit.

2 a Doctors all say the same thing: look after your heart and do regular
     _____ .

   b I'm going to teach you some _____ to improve your general fitness.

3 a Try to eat only small amounts of fatty _____ like cheese and butter.

   b I love the _____ at the new Italian restaurant.

4 a It's important to eat lots of _____ and vegetables.

   b There are several _____ that will give you lots of Vitamin C – oranges, for example.

5 a How can you enjoy _____ ? You just work all the time!

   b My colleagues all lead very interesting _____ .

6 a My office is large and crowded so _____ is a problem.

   b My computer isn't working – it's making strange _____ !

7 a My two favourite _____ are football and tennis.

   b My company has excellent facilities for _____ and leisure.

8 a This is a good year for a lot of small _____ like Lifestyle.

   b I think _____ is going to be even better next year.

3 *much, many,* and *a lot of*

Complete the sentences. Use *much*, *many*, or *a lot of*.

1 I eat _a lot of_____ fresh fruit every day.

2 My children don't eat _____ sweets or cakes.

3 Do you have _____ time for relaxation?

4 _____ fat in your diet is bad for your health.

5 There aren't _____ fitness machines at the new gym, are there?

6 I don't drink _____ alcohol – just a glass of wine at the weekend.

7 My personal trainer gave me _____ advice on keeping fit.

8 How _____ hours do you spend working at a computer each day?

❹ *much* and *many*, *a little*, and *a few*

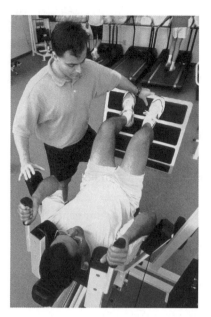

Complete the conversation. Use *How much / many* and *Only a little / a few*.

TRAINER	*How much* _____ [1] time do you spend at the gym each week?
LISA	_____ [2] . I'm very busy at work at the moment.
TRAINER	_____ [3] hours a week do you train?
LISA	_____ [4] – perhaps two hours a week.
TRAINER	That's not enough! _____ [5] other exercise do you do?
LISA	_____ [6] – but I try to go walking at the weekend.
TRAINER	_____ [7] kilometres do you usually walk?
LISA	_____ [8] , I'm afraid. I always feel tired and stressed after a week at the office.
TRAINER	Well, after a few weeks with me, you're going to reduce your stress and get your energy back!

❺ Mass and count nouns: *a*, *some*, and *any*

Complete the five conversations at the Lifestyle Restaurant. Use *a*, *some*, or *any*.

BOB	Let's go in and have *some* _____ [1] lunch.
JULES	I don't have _____ [2] money with me.
BOB	That's OK. I've got _____ [3] cash.
MARIA	Do you have _____ [4] table for four?
WAITER	Yes, of course, right here. ... Would you like _____ [5] drinks?
MARIA	Could we just have _____ [6] mineral water? Two bottles, please.
STEFI	Do you have _____ [7] vegetarian dishes?
WAITER	Yes, certainly. You'll find _____ [8] vegetarian menu on the next page.
WAITER	Would you like to order now?
JACK	Please. I'll have _____ [9] onion soup and _____ [10] chicken sandwich.
WAITER	Would you like ice and lemon with your mineral water?
JOSIE	_____ [11] ice, please, but I don't want _____ [12] lemon, thanks.

6 **Practice drills:** *any, a little, a few, much, many*

 5.1, 5.2 Follow the instructions on the Student's CD/Cassette. If necessary, refer to the Listening scripts on p.82.

Pocket Book p. 7

Pronunciation   Word stress

🎧 **5.3** Listen to the examples and notice the different stress patterns.

● ●	● ●	● ● ●
fitness	machine	calories

Put the words in the box in the correct column.

advice   culture   leisure   result   training
amount   energy   oranges   studio

● ●	● ●	● ● ●
_____	_____	_____
_____	_____	_____
_____	_____	_____

🎧 **5.3** Listen and repeat the words.

Wordpower

Food

1 Circle the word that doesn't belong in each group.

1	duck	beef	pork	~~salmon~~
2	pear	red pepper	grape	apple
3	grill	fry	cut	roast
4	chicken	tuna	prawn	sole
5	courgette	peach	cabbage	potato
6	wine	beer	cider	mineral water
7	frozen	cold	cutlet	warm
8	onion	cucumber	tomato	cheese

2 Complete the sentences. Use the words in the box.

boil   fry   grill   roast

Cooking methods

1 _____ the chicken breasts under a medium heat for twenty minutes, turning once.

2 _____ the fish in butter in a large pan for eight minutes.

3 _____ the potatoes in salted water for about fifteen minutes.

4 _____ the lamb in the oven for two hours.

③ Match the pictures to the dishes on the menu.

menu

starters

1 Warm chicken salad (slices of chicken with roast peppers, courgettes, and onions) _d_

2 Vegetable soup with fresh bread rolls ___

main courses

3 Grilled salmon and lemon sauce with fried potatoes and green beans ___

4 Roast lamb with boiled potatoes and fried aubergines ___

5 Sirloin steak with French fries and grilled tomatoes ___

desserts

6 Fresh fruit salad (pears, bananas, strawberries, grapes) ___

7 Apple pie with cream ___

8 Selection of cheeses ___

At a restaurant

Complete the two conversations. Use the phrases in the box.

> how about the main course?
> Thank you for a wonderful meal.
> Would you like some more?
> Thank you, but I couldn't eat any more.
>
> What do you recommend?
> Yes, I'd like to try that.
> Thanks. Just a little.

Conversation 1

HOST   Right. Let's order.

GUEST   Oh, I'm afraid I don't know anything about Japanese food.

_____ 1

HOST   Well, for a starter, what about *yakitori*?

GUEST   *Yakitori*? What's that?

HOST   It's small kebabs, with pieces of chicken and a vegetable called *naganegi*.

GUEST   _____ 2

HOST   Now, _____ 3
         The *shabushabu* is usually very good here.

GUEST   What's *shabushabu*?

HOST   It's thin pieces of beef and various vegetables which we cook at the table.

GUEST   Fine. I'll have that.

Conversation 2

GUEST   Mm. This drink is delicious, but it's quite strong. What is it?

HOST   *Umeshu*. It's a type of spirits made from barley and plums.

_____ 4

GUEST   _____ 5

HOST   Now, what about a dessert?

GUEST   _____ 6

HOST   Are you sure? Would you like coffee, then?

GUEST   Yes, that would be very nice.

_____ 7

HOST   You're welcome.

🎧 **5.4** Listen to the conversations and check your answers.

🎧 **5.5** Listen and repeat the phrases on the Student's CD/Cassette.

Pocket Book p. 17

UNIT 6

1 **Comparative adjectives: one syllable**

Complete the article. Use the comparative form of the adjectives in brackets.

TRAVEL

Low-cost airlines?

Are you really getting a cheap ticket when you fly with a no-frills airline?

Fares on the no-frills airlines are usually *lower* [1] (low) than on the traditional airlines, but there are other costs to think about.

Traditional airlines fly from the big airports that are _____ [2] (near) to the city centres. No-frills airlines normally use airports that are _____ [3] (far) away.

Transport to and from the big airports is _____ [4] (good), and the rail and bus services are generally _____ [5] (cheap). There is also a _____ [6] (big) choice of low-cost car parks at main airports.

No-frills airlines don't normally serve meals on the flight. You pay for sandwiches and drinks, and also for in-flight entertainment.

So the total cost of flying with a no-frills airline can be _____ [7] (high) than flying with a traditional airline. And total travelling time can be a lot _____ [8] (long).

❷ Superlative adjectives: one syllable

Look at the survey. Complete the sentences. Use the superlative form of the adjectives in brackets.

Which is the best no-frills airlines?	JumpJet	BestFlight	SkyLine
How good is the website?	✓✓✓✓	✓✓✓	✓✓✓
How cheap are the fares?	✓✓✓✓	✓✓	✓✓✓
How big is the discount for online bookings?	5%	5%	10%
How quick is the check-in time?	🕐	🕐	🕐
How long are the delays?	🕐	🕐	🕐
How new are the planes?	✓✓✓✓	✓✓✓	✓✓
How much leg room is there?	60 cm	55 cm	50 cm

JumpJet has the best _____ ¹ (good) website.

_____ ² (cheap) fares.

_____ ³ (big) discount for online bookings.

_____ ⁴ (quick) check-in time.

_____ ⁵ (long) delays.

_____ ⁶ (new) planes.

_____ ⁷ (small) amount of leg room.

❸ Comparative adjectives: *as ... as*

Look at the survey in ❷ again. Use the words in brackets to write sentences with *as ... as*.

1 *BestFlight's website is as good as SkyLine's.* _____
   (BestFlight's website / good / SkyLine's)

2 *BestFlight's fares are not as cheap as JumpJet's.* _____
   (BestFlight's fares / cheap / JumpJet's)

3 _____
   (JumpJet's discount for online bookings / big / BestFlight's)

4 _____
   (SkyLine's check-in time / quick / BestFlight's)

5 _____
   (JumpJet's delays / long / SkyLine's)

6 _____
   (SkyLine's planes / new / JumpJet's)

7 _____
   (BestFlight's amount of leg room / small / SkyLine's)

4 Comparative adjectives: two or more syllables

Look at the survey of the business-class services of four transatlantic airlines. Complete the sentences below. Use the comparative form of the adjectives in brackets and *than*.

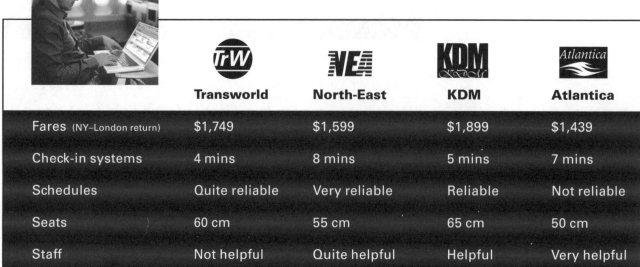

	Transworld	North-East	KDM	Atlantica
Fares (NY–London return)	$1,749	$1,599	$1,899	$1,439
Check-in systems	4 mins	8 mins	5 mins	7 mins
Schedules	Quite reliable	Very reliable	Reliable	Not reliable
Seats	60 cm	55 cm	65 cm	50 cm
Staff	Not helpful	Quite helpful	Helpful	Very helpful

1 North-East's fares are *less expensive than* (expensive) Transworld's.

2 KDM's check-in systems are _____ (efficient) Atlantica's.

3 KDM's schedules are _____ (reliable) North-East's.

4 North-East's seats are _____ (comfortable) Transworld's.

5 KDM's staff are _____ (helpful) North-East's.

5 Superlative adjectives: two or more syllables

Write sentences comparing the airline services. Use the superlative form of the adjectives in brackets.

1 *KDM's fares are the most expensive.*

  Atlantica's fares are the least expensive.

  (expensive)

2 _____

  _____

  (efficient)

3 _____

  _____

  (reliable)

4 _____

  _____

  (comfortable)

5 _____

  _____

  (helpful)

6 Superlative adjectives

Complete the magazine article. Use the superlative form of the adjectives in brackets.

CONCORDE REMEMBERED

By Will Blake

In 2003, we said goodbye to *the fastest* ¹ (fast), _____ ² (famous) and _____ ³ (beautiful) passenger airliner in the world: Concorde. For both Air France and British Airways, it was goodbye to _____ ⁴ (exciting) plane they had and _____ ⁵ (good) advertisement for their airlines.

Scientists developed _____ ⁶ (early) plans for Concorde in the 1950s. It was _____ ⁷ (important) international air project of its time. It was also one of _____ ⁸ (difficult). Commercial flights only started in 1979.

Unfortunately, Concorde could only carry 128 passengers, so the costs per passenger were _____ ⁹ (high) in the world. The air fares were _____ ¹⁰ (expensive) in the world. Only _____ ¹¹ (rich) customers could pay. The situation could not continue.

Concorde's last commercial flight was on October 24, 2003. For many of us, it was one of _____ ¹² (sad) days in flying history.

7 Practice drills: Comparative and superlative adjectives

🎧 **6.1, 6.2** Follow the instructions on the Student's CD/Cassette. If necessary, refer to the Listening scripts on p.83.

📖 Pocket Book p. 2

Pronunciation   The /ə/ sound

Read the phrases aloud and mark the main stress.

as éasy as	táller than	less expénsive than
the néwest	the most relíable	
as láte as	bétter than	more fámous than
the quíckest	the most fámous	

Read the phrases again and underline the /ə/ sound.

<u>a</u>s easy <u>a</u>s	tall<u>e</u>r th<u>a</u>n	less expensive th<u>a</u>n
th<u>e</u> new<u>e</u>st	th<u>e</u> most reli<u>a</u>ble	
as late as	better than	more famous than
the quickest	the most famous	

🎧 **6.3** Listen and repeat the phrases.

Air travel

1 Complete the sentences. Use the phrases in the box.

> duty-free shop ~~hand-luggage~~ seat-belts
> flight attendant overhead locker

1 I'm afraid you can only take one piece of _hand-luggage_ with you, Madam.

2 Have we got time to stop at the _____ and buy some cognac?

3 Could you put my bag in the _____ for me, please? I can't reach!

4 Would all passengers please make sure their _____ are fastened.

5 I'm thirsty. I'm going to ask the _____ for a drink of water.

2 Complete the word pairs. Use the words in the box.

> card luggage passport seat
> desk ~~officer~~ screen security

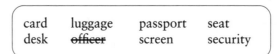

1 customs ⌐
  security ⌐ _officer_

2 arrivals ⌐
  departures ⌐ _____

3 boarding ⌐
  landing ⌐ _____

4 check-in ⌐
  information ⌐ _____

5 aisle ⌐
  window ⌐ _____

6 _____ ⌐ label
                   ⌐ trolley

7 _____ ⌐ check
                   ⌐ announcement

8 _____ ⌐ control
                   ⌐ number

3 Complete the sentences with word pairs from **2**.

1 Quick! We're late. Put all the suitcases on this _____, then let's go!

2 First, we need to go to the _____ with our luggage.

3 I'd like a _____. I want to see the view when we go over the mountains.

4 Look, our flight is showing on the _____ up there. Gate 25.

5 Flight IL8614 is boarding now. Please have your passport and _____ ready.

6 This is a _____. Please make sure that you keep your luggage with you at all times.

7 We regret that there may be delays on some flights because of the need for extra _____ at this time.

Making arrangements

Complete the telephone conversation. Use the phrases in the box.

> Could we arrange another time?   How about two o'clock?
> Is Friday morning possible for you?   When are you free?
> See you on Friday afternoon at 2.00.   No, I'm afraid I'm busy then.
> When would be convenient for you?   10 a.m. suits me fine.

STEVE   Is that Maria Pertini?

MARIA   Yes. Speaking.

STEVE   Hello, this is Steve Holmes. I'm flying to Milan later this week, so could we arrange a meeting to discuss the Elco project?

MARIA   Yes, of course. Let me see. I can see you on Thursday or Friday.

_____ 1

STEVE   _____ 2

MARIA   Yes, that's OK. Shall we say 10 o'clock?

STEVE   Yes, _____ 3

MARIA   Ah! Wait a moment. _____ 4

I've got a meeting with a client. _____

_____ 5

STEVE   Yes, of course. _____ 6

MARIA   How about Friday afternoon?

STEVE   What time would suit you?

MARIA   _____ 7

STEVE   Yes, that's fine.

MARIA   Good. _____ 8

🎧 **6.4** Listen to the conversation and check your answers.

🎧 **6.5** Listen and repeat the phrases on the Student's CD/Cassette.

 Pocket Book p. 18

UNIT 7

❶ Past Simple

Complete the magazine article. Use the Past Simple form of the verbs in brackets.

Oxfam / *the start*

This large organization _started_ [1] (start) its work in the difficult years of World War II. Back in 1942, a number of people in Oxford _met_ [2] (meet) and _____ [3] (form) a group – the **Ox**ford Committee for **Fam**ine Relief – to help people in other countries. They _____ [4] (begin) with Greece. They _____ [5] (collect) food and clothes, and _____ [6] (send) them to help many poor people in Greece.

World War II _____ [7] (come) to an end, but the group _____ [8] (see) that there was no end to wars and disasters – and the need for their work. So the organization _____ [9] (go) world-wide and its name _____ [10] (become) Oxfam. Today, Oxfam runs programmes in over 70 developing countries.

❷ Present Perfect Simple

Complete the magazine article. Use the Present Perfect form of the verbs in brackets.

Oxfam | *the success story continues*

Big successes for Oxfam _have included_ [1] (include) help after hurricanes and other natural disasters. There _____ [2] (be) another important aim, too. From the start, Oxfam _____ [3] (work) to help poor people build a better future. It _____ [4] (organize) long-term programmes in developing countries for many years, and these _____ [5] (help) millions of people to escape poverty and disease. For example, Oxfam _____ [6] (provide) equipment for communities to get clean water. It _____ [7] (train) thousands of health workers, and these people _____ [8] (improve) the health of whole regions. In addition, Oxfam _____ [9] (make) many new businesses possible through financial help and training. Recently, with some skills training, a group of women in Bangladesh _____ [10] (build) a successful company making hand-made products. ∎

❸ Irregular verbs

Complete the table with the correct form of the verbs.

Infinitive	Past Simple	Past Participle
break	broke	_broken_
buy	_____	_____
_____	cost	_____
drink	_____	_____
_____	_____	eaten
_____	fell	_____
forget	_____	_____
_____	found	_____
give	_____	_____
_____	_____	had
hear	_____	_____
_____	hit	_____
know	_____	_____
_____	_____	lost
put	_____	_____
_____	rose	_____
_____	_____	sold
shut	_____	_____
_____	understood	_____
_____	_____	worn

Make a similar table for the ten irregular verbs in ❶ and ❷.

❹ Past Simple and Present Perfect Simple

Underline the correct form of the verbs.

1 In recent years, the rich *became* / _have become_ richer.

2 At the same time, the poor *grew* / *have grown* poorer.

3 In 1945, the richer countries of the world *started* / *have started* the World Bank to help the poorer parts of the world.

4 Since 1945, most developing countries *borrowed* / *have borrowed* from the World Bank to pay for development programmes.

5 People in the Third World *received* / *have received* aid such as food from western countries for many years.

6 Until the 1980s, the development and aid programmes *were often* / *have often been* the wrong ones for developing countries; for example, free food aid *often hurt* / *has often hurt* local farmers financially.

7 There is another problem even now – western businesses *continued* / *have continued* to buy from the country with the lowest price.

8 In the last twenty years, organizations like Tradecraft *finally began* / *have finally begun* to make a real difference to the way western and developing countries trade.

⑤ Past Simple and Present Perfect Simple

Complete the article. Use the Past Simple or the Present Perfect Simple form of the verbs in brackets.

Concern | *in partnership with* **Oxfam**

In 1975, the organization Concern *established* _____¹ (establish) a centre in Demra, Bangladesh. Concern _____² (want) to provide food and health care for poor people. Since then, with the help of Oxfam, it _____³ (encourage) people to work together to improve their living conditions.

For several years, Oxfam and Concern _____⁴ (work) with a group of women in Demra. In the 1990s, Concern _____⁵ (set) up a skills training centre and the women _____⁶ (learn) to make hand-made products like baskets and incense. At first, the women _____⁷ (sell) their products locally. Then Oxfam _____⁸ (do) some market research for them. Since then, the business _____⁹ (develop) its incense products for the international market. In recent years, it _____¹⁰ (sell) its incense to The Body Shop and other European buyers. The business _____¹¹ (change) the lives of 150 women and their families. ■

6 Present Perfect Simple questions

Anton Lim was interviewed about the problems faced by his small business in Jakarta. Write the interviewer's questions. Use the words in brackets and the Present Perfect Simple form.

INTERVIEWER	_How long has your workshop been in business?_ 1
	(how long / your workshop / be / in business)
LIM	We've been here for about three years – since 2001.
INTERVIEWER	_____ 2
	(the economic crisis / affect / your business)
LIM	Yes, it has. People don't have much money to spend.
INTERVIEWER	_____ 3
	(you / have / financial problems)
LIM	Yes, we have. It's been very hard to continue in business.
INTERVIEWER	_____ 4
	(where / sell / your products up to now)
LIM	We've sold in local markets and through shops in Jakarta.
INTERVIEWER	_____ 5
	(you / think about / selling outside Indonesia)
LIM	No, we haven't. Is it possible?
INTERVIEWER	Yes. Your products are good and I'm sure the Fairtrade organization would like to help you.

7 Practice drills: Present Perfect Simple, Past Simple

🎧 **7.1, 7.2** Follow the instructions on the Student's CD/Cassette. If necessary, refer to the Listening scripts on p.84.

 Pocket Book pp. 10, 13

Pronunciation   **Past Simple and Present Perfect Simple**

🎧 **7.3** Listen to the sentences. Which tense do you hear? Write *PS* for the Past Simple, and *PPS* for the Present Perfect Simple.

1	_PPS_	5	____
2	_PS_	6	____
3	____	7	____
4	____	8	____

Wordpower

The language of graphs

1 Look at the chart. Complete the sentences. Use *at*, *by*, *in*, *of*, *from*, and *to*.

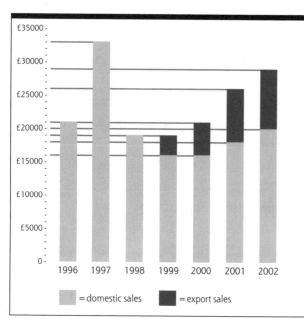

= domestic sales   = export sales

1 In 1997, domestsic sales rose dramatically *from* $21,000 *to* $33,000.

2 In 1998, there was a big fall _____ domestic sales – they went down _____ just $19,000.

3 There was another fall _____ $3,000 _____ domestic sales in 1999.

4 Export sales started in 1999, so total sales for that year remained stable _____ $19,000.

5 In 2000, export sales increased _____ 66%.

6 In 2001, there was a small increase _____ domestic sales _____ $18,000.

7 Export sales also rose _____ $5,000 in 2001.

8 In 2002, there was a rise _____ $3,000 _____ total sales: sales went up _____ $26,000 _____ $29,000.

2 Complete the tables.

Verb	Noun	Adjective	Adverb
decrease	*a decrease*	dramatic	_____
fall	_____	sharp	_____
improve	_____	slight	_____
increase	_____	steady	_____
rise	_____		

3 Change the sentences to give the same meaning. Use the words in **2**.

1 There has been a sharp fall in UK sales.
   UK sales *have fallen sharply* _____.

2 Sales to the US have risen dramatically.
   There *has been a dramatic rise* _____ in sales to the US.

3 The cost of energy has decreased steadily.
   There _____ in the cost of energy.

4 There has been a sharp fall in other production costs.
   Other production costs _____.

5 There has been a steady improvement in production quality.
   Production quality _____.

6 There has been a slight decrease in staff numbers.
   Staff numbers _____.

7 Working conditions have improved dramatically.
   There _____ in working conditions.

8 Average pay has increased slightly.
   There _____ in average pay.

46 ● UNIT 7

Opinions and suggestions

Complete the two conversations between Anne and her colleagues, Carl and Yvette. Use the phrases in the box.

I'm not sure about that.	why don't you get a job abroad
In my opinion,	Yes, that's a good idea.
What do you think about that?	Why not travel round
Any ideas on	I think

Conversation 1

ANNE   I'm happy in my job, but I'd like a new challenge.

_____ ¹ what I can do?

CARL   _____ ² the world for a year?

ANNE   I don't just want to travel. I'd like to really get to know another country and learn about their culture.

CARL   Well, _____ ³

for a year or two? You could help people in the Third World and learn about their culture, too.

ANNE   _____ ⁴ I'll talk to my boss about it.

Conversation 2

YVETTE   What did your boss say?

ANNE   He's given me unpaid leave for a year.

YVETTE   That's good of him! What do you plan to do?

ANNE   I'm going to work for Oxfam and help build new schools in Guatemala. _____ ⁵

YVETTE   _____ ⁶ it's a bad career move.

You can return to your job, but _____ ⁷

you're going to lose opportunities for promotion.

ANNE   _____ ⁸

The company hopes to expand into Latin America. My boss says it could be very useful experience.

🎧 **7.4** Listen to the conversations and check your answers.

🎧 **7.5** Listen and repeat the phrases on the Student's CD/Cassette.

 Pocket Book p. 20

UNIT 8

Language focus **1** *may, might, should, have to, be important to*

Lucy Taylor works in Germany, but she is back in the UK on holiday. She is talking to Sam Bridges, who is thinking of getting a job in Germany. Read the conversation and underline the correct verb forms.

SAM   I suppose you *may / have to* [1] be very formal at work?

LUCY   Yes and no. It's *important to / important not to* [2] be formal at meetings, and you *may / may not* [3] find that your boss is quite formal. But my office colleagues are very informal. We *may / don't have to* [4] wear business suits, for example. We just wear jeans.

SAM   Tell me more about formal meetings. I hear that it's *important to / important not to* [5] make jokes, and everybody *has to / shouldn't* [6] be very serious.

LUCY   A few jokes at the beginning are fine. But when the real work starts, people *may not / shouldn't* [7] continue to laugh and joke. I know that British visitors sometimes do, but in general, Germans don't like it much. In fact, some Germans *might / might not* [8] even get angry!

SAM   What about outside work? What *may / should* [9] I do to meet people?

LUCY   I often go out with people from work. But in the north of Germany that *doesn't have to / may not* [10] happen because people don't usually mix work and social life. You could join one or two clubs when you move to the area.

❷ *may, might, should, have to, be important to*

Read the extract from a guide to working in Japan. Then complete the sentences below. Use the pairs of verbs in the box.

> be important to / be important not to   have to / not have to
> may / may not   might / might not   should / shouldn't

Working in Japan

Finding work You don't need a visa for a visit to find work in Japan. You can go there as a tourist. When you get a job, you need a work visa before you can start work. You can't get this in Japan. But it isn't necessary to return home to apply for a work visa. You just need to take a short flight to Korea, Japan's nearest neighbour. You can get a work visa there.

Doing business When you go on a business trip to Japan, it's a good idea to take some English–Japanese business cards. These are important, and it's certainly not a good idea to leave them at your hotel when you go to a meeting!

It's very possible that your Japanese colleagues won't agree to a business deal on your first trip. They will want to get to know you first. It's very possible that they will invite you out to eat or drink with them in the evening. Don't try to make your Japanese colleagues complete a business deal before they're ready. They need time to talk to everyone in the company.

It's possible that a Japanese colleague will invite you to his home, but this doesn't often happen. It's possible that he won't invite you to meet his family even after twenty or thirty years! Don't worry about this. It's normal for the Japanese to keep their family and working lives separate.

1 You *don't have to* _____ get a visa for a visit to find work in Japan, but you *have to* _____ get a work visa before you can start your new job.

2 You _____ get a work visa in your own country. You just _____ fly to Korea to get one.

3 You _____ get some business cards for a business trip, and you _____ forget them when you go to a meeting.

4 Your Japanese colleagues _____ agree to a business deal on your first trip, but they _____ invite you out so they can get to know you.

5 It _____ try to complete a business deal before your Japanese colleagues are ready. It _____ give them time to talk to everyone in the company.

6 A Japanese colleague _____ invite you to his home, but this is not very likely. It _____ happen even after many years of doing business together.

❸ *should, have to, may*

Write sentences about doing business in the USA. Use a modal verb that adds the meaning in brackets.

1 *You have to wear a business suit at meetings.*

   wear / a business suit / at meetings (It's obligatory)

2 _____

   make / small talk / at the beginning of meetings (It's a good idea)

3 _____

   exchange / business cards / with each other (It's not necessary)

4 _____

   do business / on the golf course (It's possible)

5 _____

   learn / the job titles of everyone in the company (It's necessary)

6 _____

   give / expensive gifts / to your host (It's not a good idea)

❹ Mistakes with modal verbs

Some of the sentences below have a grammatical mistake. Find the mistakes. Write correct sentences where necessary.

1 Should I arrive before 10.00?
   (correct)

2 You should to read this book.
   You should read this book.

3 He doesn't have to write the report.

   _____

4 Do they might fly home tomorrow?

   _____

5 Rosa may not buy the car.

   _____

6 They have to not go. It's a holiday.

   _____

7 Andreas may to leave the company.

   _____

8 Should he going to Milan?

   _____

9 She have to call me back tomorrow.

   _____

10 Felipe shoulds arrange a meeting.

   _____

❺ Practice drill: *should* and *have to*

🎧 8.1 Follow the instructions on the Student's CD/Cassette. If necessary, refer to the Listening script on p.85.

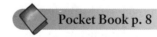
Pocket Book p. 8

Wordpower

Word building

 Read the employer's references for members of his staff. Underline the correct adjectives and nouns.

Dear Mr Klein

Ms Cristina Lorca: letter of reference

I am happy to provide a reference for Ms Lorca, who has applied for the post of Administration Officer with your company.

During her three years with us, Ms Lorca has shown her *adaptable / adaptability* [1] as she has managed a wide range of tasks very well. Recently, we gave her a very *important / importance* [2] role in our move to a new data control system. The change was completely *successful / success* [3], and there were no technical problems. The *successful / success* [4] of that project was due to Ms Lorca's hard work.

Dear Ms Silvestrini

Mr Flavio Gianetti: letter of reference

I am pleased to support Mr Gianetti's application for the position of Regional Marketing Manager with your company.

During his five years with us, Mr Gianetti has shown real *ambitious / ambition* [5] and has moved up from management trainee to become our youngest area manager. During these difficult economic times, he has used his *creative / creativity* [6] to find new answers to old problems. He is highly *organized / organization* [7] and always plans his time and work carefully. Earlier this year he was responsible for the *organized / organization* [8] of a very successful advertising campaign for our company.

2 Read what the people say about themselves. Then match four of the adjectives in the box to each person.

~~ambitious~~   efficient   insensitive   unambitious
creative   honest   reliable   unpunctual
disorganized   impatient   sociable   unsociable

My good points

I want to be successful at work and get a top job in the company. I usually do tasks quickly and well, and get them right first time.

Armand

My bad points

I get angry when other people are slow. Friends tell me that I often say the wrong thing and hurt other people's feelings.

I love my job as an interior designer – I have to think of great new ideas for people's homes. I spend a lot of time with other people when I'm working, and I really enjoy that.

Maria

I'm never on time for meetings. And my studio is very untidy, so I often can't find things. That's why I'm late for so many meetings!

I build kitchens. I tell customers what I can do for them and when, and I do exactly that. And I always charge a fair price.

Jason

My brother wants me to make my one-man business into a company, but I don't want anything big like that. I like living and working alone – people are too much trouble!

Armand: *ambitious*, _____

Maria: _____

Jason: _____

Invitations

Two German colleagues are talking to Lucy soon after her start at Koenig Auto GmbH in south Germany. Complete the conversation. Use the phrases in the box.

> How about
> Would you join me
> why don't you come with us?
> Would you like to join us?
>
> Thanks a lot, but
> I'd love to, but I'm afraid I can't.
> Thank you. I'd enjoy that very much.

DIETER   How was your first week, Lucy?

LUCY   You do things differently here, but everyone has been very helpful.

DIETER   Good. We're all going out for a meal after work.
_____ 1

LUCY   _____ 2 You see, I promised my new neighbours I'd go to their barbecue at 6.00.

HELGA   Oh, that's a pity. … I'm going into town tomorrow morning.
_____ 3 there for lunch? I could show you the old castle in the afternoon.

LUCY   _____ 4 I'm meeting an old college friend in Munich tomorrow. Sorry!

HELGA   No problem. What about Sunday? Some of us are going on a trip to the Bodensee – that's Lake Constance in English.
_____ 5 joining us?

LUCY   That sounds nice.

DIETER   Yes, it's beautiful at this time of year, so
_____ 6

LUCY   Are you sure?

HELGA   Yes, of course. You're very welcome.

LUCY   _____ 7

DIETER   Good. We'll pick you up at 8.30 on Sunday morning.

🎧 **8.3** Listen to the conversation and check your answers.

🎧 **8.4** Listen and repeat the phrases on the Student's CD/Cassette.

 Pocket Book p. 18

UNIT 9

1 Present Perfect Simple and Past Simple

Complete the magazine article. Use the Past Simple or the Present Perfect Simple form of the verbs in brackets.

A Firm in Full Flower
The Story of Fresh Bouquets

Fresh Bouquets is a small company, but in the last few years it _has become_ ¹ (become) a big success story. Entrepreneurs Graham Hodson and Shaun Caulfield _____ ² (found) the company in 1991. Since then, they _____ ³ (develop) a very good market for last-minute gifts of flowers. In the last four years, they _____ ⁴ (increase) sales by over 100% per year, from £740,000 to £6.4 million.

At first, Fresh Bouquets _____ ⁵ (grow) its own supplies of flowers at its base in south-east England. Soon, the company _____ ⁶ (need) to import flowers from other countries, such as Turkey and Kenya.

Their first big problem _____ ⁷ (be) the short life of cut flowers, and this _____ ⁸ (remain) the biggest challenge up to the present time. Every day, flowers travel perhaps thousands of kilometres and have to reach the company's 4,500 customers – mainly petrol stations and supermarkets – in top condition. So, several years ago, the company _____ ⁹ (decide) to spend £500,000 a year on information technology for its distribution system. It _____ ¹⁰ (continue) to invest this amount each year since then.

However, all the hard work and investment _____ ¹¹ (produce) great results. At the beginning of this year, Fresh Bouquets _____ ¹² (appear) at number 27 in the list of Britain's 100 fastest-growing companies.

❷ Present Perfect Simple and Present Perfect Continuous

Read the magazine article. Underline the correct verb forms.

The island of Murano is the glass-making capital of Venice. Skilled craftsmen *have made* / <u>*have been making*</u>[1] glass there since the thirteenth century. The Gabino family *has had* / *has been having*[2] a family-run business on Murano for about 300 years. The business *has developed* / *has been developing*[3] many different glass products in its long history. For the past 50 years, it *has produced* / *has been producing*[4] glass beads, the famous 'perles di Venezia' (Venetian pearls). Making the beads is a very skilled job. Aldo Gabino *has learned* / *has been learning*[5] the art of bead-making for five years. He *has designed* / *has been designing*[6] a number of fine pieces of jewellery during this time. He *has shown* / *has been showing*[7] these at several important exhibitions in Venice. For the past few weeks, Aldo *has worked* / *has been working*[8] on a collection of jewellery based on traditional designs. He hopes these will be ready for the famous Venice Carnival in February.

❸ Present Perfect Simple and Present Perfect Continuous

Read the situations. Use the words in brackets to write one sentence using the Present Perfect Simple and one sentence using the Present Perfect Continuous.

1 Alain is at his computer. He has to produce five sales reports this afternoon.

   a <u>*He has been writing reports since 1 p.m.*</u>
     (write reports since 1 p.m.)

   b _____ (write two reports so far)

2 Stefan often gives presentations for his company. He is at a sales conference today.

   a _____
     (speak for 45 minutes)

   b _____ (give three presentations this week)

3 Maria uses English in her work and sometimes makes business trips to the UK.

   a _____ (learn English for five years)

   b _____ (visit the UK twice this year)

4 Louise is visiting customers today. She has to see ten customers.

   a _____ (drive round town all morning)

   b _____ (see four customers so far)

5 Pablo is a marketing manager for a wine-making company.

   a _____
     (work in the wine industry since he left college)

   b _____
     (work for three different companies since he left college)

❹ Time expressions: general

Complete the interview with Masako Coxeter, a Japanese interpreter living in the UK. Use *for*, *since*, *in*, or *at*.

INTERVIEWER Have you been living in the UK *for* ¹ a long time?

MASAKO I moved from Tokyo with my husband _____ ² 1992, so, yes, I've been here _____ ³ a number of years.

INTERVIEWER What have you been doing _____ ⁴ you moved to the UK?

MASAKO I worked for a translation agency in London until 1999.

INTERVIEWER What have you been doing _____ ⁵ then?

MASAKO I've been running my own translation business. I've also been interpreting for Japanese scientists _____ ⁶ the last two years.

INTERVIEWER Do you ever go back to Japan?

MASAKO Yes, I do. I like to be with my parents in Japan _____ ⁷ New Year. I sometimes go again _____ ⁸ the spring, too. The weather is very nice _____ ⁹ that time of year.

❺ Time expressions: *for* and *since*

Look at the calendar. Today's date is 30 August. Change the sentences to give the same meaning. Use the words in brackets.

January	February	March	April	May	June	July	August	September	October	November	December
1	**1**	1	1	**1**	1	1	**1**	1	1	1	1
2	2	2	2	**2**	2	2	2	2	**2**	2	2
3	3	3	**3**	3	3	**3**	3	3	**3**	3	3
4	4	4	**4**	4	4	**4**	4	**4**	4	4	**4**
5	5	5	5	5	5	**5**	5	**5**	5	5	**5**
6	6	**6**	6	6	**6**	6	6	6	6	**6**	6
7	**7**	**7**	7	7	7	7	**7**	7	7	**7**	7
8	**8**	8	8	**8**	8	8	**8**	8	8	8	8
9	9	9	9	**9**	9	9	9	9	**9**	9	9
10	10	10	**10**	10	10	**10**	10	10	**10**	10	10
11	11	11	**11**	11	11	11	**11**	**11**	11	11	**11**
12	12	12	12	12	**12**	12	12	**12**	12	12	**12**
13	13	**13**	13	13	**13**	13	13	13	13	**13**	13
14	**14**	**14**	14	14	14	14	**14**	14	14	**14**	14
15	**15**	15	15	**15**	15	15	**15**	15	15	15	15
16	16	16	16	**16**	16	16	16	16	**16**	16	16
17	17	17	**17**	17	17	**17**	17	17	**17**	17	17
18	18	18	**18**	18	18	**18**	18	**18**	18	18	**18**
19	19	19	19	19	**19**	19	19	**19**	19	19	**19**
20	20	**20**	20	20	**20**	20	20	20	20	**20**	20
21	**21**	**21**	21	21	21	21	**21**	21	21	**21**	21
22	**22**	22	22	**22**	22	22	**22**	22	22	22	22
23	23	23	23	**23**	23	23	23	23	**23**	23	23
24	24	24	**24**	24	24	**24**	24	24	**24**	24	24
25	25	25	**25**	25	25	**25**	25	**25**	25	25	**25**
26	26	26	26	26	**26**	26	26	**26**	26	26	**26**
27	27	**27**	27	27	**27**	27	27	27	27	**27**	27
28	**28**	**28**	28	28	28	28	**28**	28	28	**28**	28
29	**29**	29	29	**29**	29	29	**29**	29	29	29	29
30		30	30	**30**	30	30	(30)	30	**30**	30	3
31		31				**31**	31		**31**		31

1 Sales have been rising since the end of April. (for)
   Sales have been rising for four months.

2 Susan has been travelling for ten days. (since)
   _____

3 Silvie and Tomas have been business partners since August 1999. (for)
   _____

4 Blanca-Maria has been working in Poland for six months. (since)
   _____

5 James has been away since 25 August. (for)
   _____

6 Time expressions: *for* and *since*

Complete the sentences to make true statements about yourself.

1 I have been living in ———————————————
 for ————————————— .

2 I have been learning ———————————————
 since ————————————— .

3 I have been interested in ———————————————
 for ————————————— .

4 I have been going to ———————————————
 since ————————————— .

5 I have been trying to ———————————————
 for ————————————— .

6 I have been trying not to ———————————————
 since ————————————— .

7 Practice drills: Present Perfect Continuous

🎧 **9.1, 9.2** Follow the instructions on the Student's CD/Cassette. If necessary, refer to the Listening scripts on pp.85, 86.

> Pocket Book pp. 13, 14, 16

Wordpower

Word families

1 Complete the table of word families.

Verb	Noun	
	(activity, thing)	(person)
———	competition	———
consume	———	———
———	———	developer
———	———	distributor
———	———	economist
———	industry	———
invest	———	———
operate	———	———
———	———	organizer
translate	———	———

Collocations

2 Complete the collocations. Use the words in the box.

> countries   goods   management
> ~~free market~~   industrial   mass

1 *free-market* economy
2 developing _____
3 _____ skills
4 _____ development
5 consumer _____
6 _____ production

3 Complete the sentences. Use the collocations in **2**.

1 Last year saw a 10 per cent rise in the sale of _____ – the biggest rise was in electrical items for the home.

2 New business graduates entering the company have to take a course on _____, so that they can learn how to run a big organization successfully.

3 The price of goods and services is not controlled by the government in a _____, so prices rise and fall depending on supply and demand.

4 Water shortages and diseases are still very big problems in _____ trying to improve their economic situation and the health of their people.

5 There has been a lot of _____ in recent years – several factories have been opened on a new site to the north of the city.

6 Many companies continue to use a system of _____ so that they can make large numbers of goods and sell them at a cheaper price to the public.

Offers and requests

Helen is getting ready for her trip to Chicago. Complete the two conversations. Use the phrases in the box.

Shall I drive you	Would you be able to meet me
would you like me to call	I'm sorry, but that's not possible.
if you like, I could	Yes, of course.
could you	Thank you. I'd appreciate that.
Would you mind	That's very kind of you, but

Conversation 1

HELEN   I have to check in for my flight to Chicago in an hour, so

_____ 1

print out this report and distribute it? I don't have time.

TONY   Yes, certainly. _____ 2 to the airport?

HELEN   _____ 3

it's more important for you to be here.

TONY   Well, _____ 4 a taxi?

HELEN   _____ 5

Could we say ten minutes from now?

Conversation 2

HELEN   Hi, Sandra. I'm arriving in Chicago at 16.45 local time.

_____ 6

at the airport? Then we could talk on the way to the hotel.

SANDRA   _____ 7

I have an important meeting.

HELEN   OK, no problem. _____ 8

sending a car to meet me?

SANDRA   _____ 9 I'll arrange that right now.

And _____ 10

meet you later at the hotel.

HELEN   Great. Let's meet at 8.00 and have dinner together.

SANDRA   That's fine. See you soon, and have a good trip.

🎧 **9.4** Listen to the conversations and check your answers.

🎧 **9.5** Listen and repeat the phrases on the Student's CD/Cassette.

 Pocket Book p. 20

UNIT 10

Language focus

❶ Future: *will*

Match a phrase from each column to make sentences about the possible problems of global warming in the future.

1 *Global warming*	will melt	their homes.
2 Summers	will lose	*the world's climate.*
3 Higher temperatures	will disappear	the Arctic ice.
4 Sea levels	*will change*	hotter and drier.
5 People in coastal areas	will become	by up to seven metres.
6 Cities in coastal areas	will rise	under water.

1 *Global warming will change the world's climate.*

2 _____

3 _____

4 _____

5 _____

6 _____

❷ Certainty and uncertainty

Use the words in brackets to write questions to ask someone about their future.

1 *Do you think you will live abroad* _____ ?

(live abroad)

2 _____ ?

(work from home)

3 _____ ?

(do your shopping online)

4 _____ ?

(have more leisure time than today)

5 _____ ?

(learn a new language)

6 _____ ?

(send all your letters by email)

7 _____ ?

(do more for the environment than now)

Now match the questions to the answers below.

a Yes, I'm sure I will. I plan to start working part-time next year. _____

b No, I'm sure I won't. I like to look at things before I choose what to buy. _____

c Maybe. I'm not sure. It's more personal if you write using pen and paper. _____

d Yes, I think so. I should recycle glass and plastic, and try to use my car less. _____

e No, I don't think so. I don't want to move away from my family and friends. _1_

f Maybe. I'm not very sure. I speak English, Spanish, and Russian now. _____

g Definitely not! I like to work with other people and I'm too disorganized to run my own office. _____

❸ Future: *will* questions

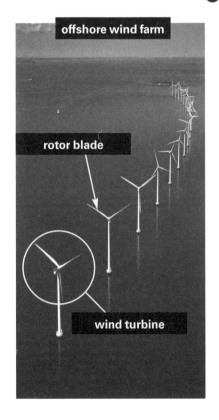

offshore wind farm

rotor blade

wind turbine

A reporter is asking an engineer about the world's largest new offshore* wind farm near the coast of Ireland, at Arklow. Use the words in brackets to write the questions.

REPORTER *Where will the wind farm be* _____ ¹?
(be / the wind farm / where / will)

ENGINEER It will be ten kilometres out at sea, sixty kilometres south of Dublin.

REPORTER _____ ²?
(will / to operate / the wind farm / when / start)

ENGINEER The first stage will start to produce power in four years.

REPORTER _____ ³?
(will / they construct / how many / wind turbines)

ENGINEER There are plans to construct 200.

REPORTER _____ ⁴?
(be / the wind turbines / will / how big)

ENGINEER Huge! Each rotor blade will be 104 metres long.

REPORTER _____ ⁵?
(be / the wind farm / to build / will / very expensive)

ENGINEER Yes, it certainly will. It will cost about €630 million.

REPORTER _____ ⁶?
(electricity / it produce / how much / will)

ENGINEER Up to 520 Megawatts – 10 per cent of Ireland's power.

REPORTER _____ ⁷?
(there be / more offshore wind farms / will)

ENGINEER Yes. Denmark has already built some small ones, and a lot of countries plan to build large wind farms.

*offshore: in the sea, at a distance from the coast

❹ 1st Conditional

Mark and Kay want to buy a new car, but they have very different ideas. Read the points for and against each car. Then complete the conversation. Use *'ll* or *won't*.

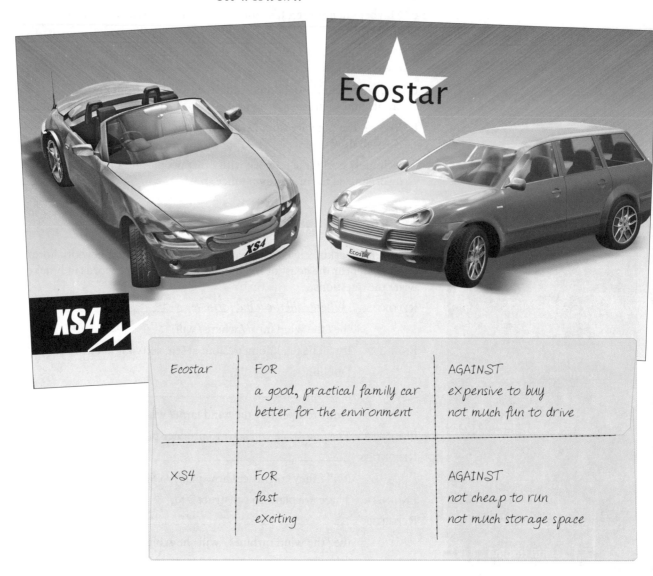

Ecostar	FOR	AGAINST
	a good, practical family car	expensive to buy
	better for the environment	not much fun to drive
XS4	FOR	AGAINST
	fast	not cheap to run
	exciting	not much storage space

KAY   I think we should buy an Ecostar.

MARK   Really? If we get an Ecostar, it <u>won't</u> [1] be much fun to drive. If we get an XS4, it _____ [2] be much more exciting.

KAY   I agree – if we buy an XS4, it _____ [3] be faster and more fun …

MARK   Great!

KAY   … but if we get an XS4, it _____ [4] have much storage space – there are going to be three of us soon! If we choose an Ecostar, it _____ [5] be a good, practical family car.

MARK   Boring! And if we choose one of those Eco things, it _____ [6] be expensive to buy.

KAY   But if we have an XS4, it _____ [7] be cheap to run – they use a lot of fuel. It _____ [8] be better for the environment if we buy an Ecostar.

❺ 1st Conditional

Write 1st Conditional sentences about Mark and Kay. Use the words in brackets.

1 *If Mark agrees with Kay, they'll buy an Ecostar.*

(Mark agree with Kay / they buy an Ecostar)

2 *They won't get an XS4 if Kay wins the argument.*

(they not get an XS4 / Kay win the argument)

3 _____

(they choose an Ecostar / it expensive to buy)

4 _____

(they spend a lot on fuel / they decide to get an XS4)

5 _____

(they choose an XS4 / there not be much room for their baby)

6 _____

(they have a lot of storage space / they get an Ecostar)

7 _____

(they buy an Ecostar / they help the environment)

❻ Practice drills: 1st Conditional

🎧 **10.1** Follow the instructions on the Student's CD/Cassette. If necessary, refer to the Listening script on p.86.

 Pocket Book p. 2

Pronunciation *will* and *'ll*

Complete the conversation with *'ll* or *will*.

REPORTER   It's a fantastic project. Do you think it *'ll* ___ [1] succeed?

ENGINEER   Oh, yes, we're sure it *will* ___ [2].

REPORTER   _____ [3] the wind farm be very big?

ENGINEER   Yes, it _____ [4] be about 36 kilometres long.

REPORTER   _____ [5] people be able to see it from the coast?

ENGINEER   Yes, they _____ [6], but not easily. The turbines _____ [7] be a long way from the coast.

REPORTER   I suppose there _____ [8] be damage to wildlife.

ENGINEER   No, we don't think there _____ [9]. We're making sure there _____ [10] be very little.

🎧 **10.2** Listen and check your answers.

🎧 **10.3** Listen and repeat phrases with *will* and *'ll* from the conversation.

Prepositions of place

Say where things are in the picture. Use the prepositions in the box and the words in brackets.

above	between	in front of	on the left of	next to
behind	in	on	on the right of	under

1   *The reception desk is on the left of the reception area.*
    (reception desk / reception area)

2   _____
    (sales office / reception area)

3   _____
    (Kay / sofa)

4   _____
    (Mark / sofa)

5   _____
    (coffee table / Kay)

6   _____
    (rubbish bin / coffee table)

7   _____
    (coffee machine / photocopier and water cooler)

8   _____
    (phone / computer keyboard)

9   _____
    (showroom sign / showroom entrance)

10 _____
    (Mark's and Kay's new car / showroom)

Asking for information

Julia Carr has just finished a Business Management course in the UK and is on the phone to careers adviser Kate Dee. Complete the conversation with the phrases in the box.

Can you tell me	Could you repeat that, please?
Could you tell me how	I'm afraid I don't have much information
Do you know what	about that.
Right, I've got that.	I'd like some information about
I'll look that up.	

KATE So, you want to spend the summer at an environmental work camp. Is that right?

JULIA Yes. _____ 1 camps in Spain or Portugal.

KATE What about Sungrow Desert Technology? They're based in Cambridge, but they have a big environmental project in the south of Spain.

JULIA That sounds interesting. _____ 2 to contact them?

KATE _____ 3

Right, you can contact them by post or by email.

JULIA _____ 4 their email address?

KATE It's sungrow@clara.net.

JULIA _____ 5

KATE Of course. It's sungrow@clara.net.

JULIA _____ 6 kind of work they do?

KATE _____ 7

It just says that they work on farming techniques for very dry regions. I suggest you find out from their website. It's sundestec.org.uk.

JULIA _____ 8 Thanks for your help.

KATE You're very welcome.

🎧 **10.4** Listen to the conversation and check your answers.

🎧 **10.5** Listen and repeat the phrases on the Student's CD/Cassette.

 Pocket Book p. 17

UNIT 11

Language focus   **❶ 2nd Conditional**

Complete the newspaper report about why some people continue to use their cars for work. Use the Past Simple or 2nd Conditional form of the verbs in brackets.

Monster traffic jam

... and it took until midnight for traffic in and around the city to start moving again. *Some of the unhappy commuters had these things to say.*

Peter McFall, a sales manager, took seven hours to travel 15 kilometres home from work. He said, 'I have to travel into the city centre. If I _communicated_ ¹ (communicate) with clients just by email and phone, I _would lose_ ² (lose) business. If the government _____ ³ (provide) a really good public transport system, we _____ ⁴ (not have) these huge traffic jams.'

Andrea di Stefano, a working mother, said, 'I hate driving in traffic, but if I _____ ⁵ (travel) by public transport, my life _____ ⁶ (get) even more difficult. I have to take my child to and from school. I might also have to go to the bank or the supermarket on my way home. If I _____ ⁷ (rely) on public transport, I _____ ⁸ (not be able) to do all these things.'

Dipak Nandy, a bank worker, said, 'If the price of public transport _____ ⁹ (not be) so high, I _____ ¹⁰ (use) it more.' He also said, 'If trains and buses _____ ¹¹ (arrive) on time, people _____ ¹² (not complain) so much.'

❷ 2nd Conditional

Some city councillors are discussing possible answers to the problem of traffic congestion. Write 2nd Conditional statements. Use the words in brackets.

1 *If our public transport system was efficient, more people would use it.*

(our public transport system be efficient / more people use it)

2 *The system would be more efficient if we integrated the buses and trains.*

(the system be more efficient / we integrate the buses and trains)

3 _____

(we introduce a light-rail system / it reduce car traffic)

4 _____

   _____

(commuters use a single ticket for all journeys / they can change easily from one route to another)

5 _____

(public transport be more popular / we reduce the cost)

6 _____

(we introduce a congestion charge / fewer motorists drive into the city)

7 _____

   _____

(people leave their cars outside the city / we provide free car parks and buses)

8 _____

(more people use bikes / this reduce traffic congestion)

9 _____

(more people cycle to work / we create safe cycle lanes)

10 _____

(we encourage car-sharing schemes / there be a lot less traffic)

❸ Advice with 2nd Conditionals

A colleague wants to visit just one city in your country. Give him/her some advice. Use *If I were you, I would / wouldn't … .*

1 what city to visit

   _____

2 where to stay

   _____

3 which interesting place to go

   _____

4 which place not to go

   _____

5 where to go for the best traditional food

   _____

6 what to be careful not to do

   _____

❹ 2nd Conditional questions

Shanghai hopes to build a 'city in the sky'. This would help reduce traffic congestion and save a lot of space. Complete the questions. Use the Past Simple or 2nd Conditional form of the verbs in brackets.

1 If we _built_ (build) the 'city in the sky', _would it be_ (it / be) the tallest building in the world?

2 How many people _would live_ (live) there if we _decided_ (decide) to have the maximum number of floors?

3 If the building _____ (have) a lot of living space, _____ (there / be) room for other things?

4 If somebody _____ (live) at the top, how long _____ (it / take) to get up there?

5 What _____ (people / do) if a fire _____ (start)?

6 _____ (the building / be) safe if an earthquake _____ (hit) the city?

7 If we _____ (agree) to go ahead, how long _____ (the building work / take)?

Now match the questions to the answers below.

a They would escape to the next floor up or down. _____

b About fifteen years for the whole project. _____

c The lifts would go straight to the top in less than two minutes. _____

d Yes. It would be 1,140 metres high – three times bigger than the Eiffel Tower! _1_

e About 100,000. _____

f Yes, because the building would go 200 metres down into the ground. _____

g Yes – there would be hotels, offices, shopping centres, and even parks. _____

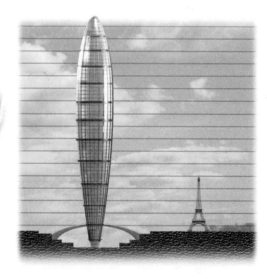

❺ Conditional sentences: likely and unlikely situations

What would you do in the likely and unlikely situations below? Write 1st Conditional or 2nd Conditional sentences.

1 You get the salary rise that you want. (possible and likely)

   If I get the salary rise I want, I'll

2 Your company offers you the top job in its New York office. (possible but not likely)

3 Some friends at work invite you for a meal on Friday. (possible and likely).

4 You win two round-the-world air tickets. (possible but not likely)

5 You have some free time next month. (possible and likely)

6 You meet an old school friend on holiday. (possible but not likely)

7 Someone in your English class suggests an end-of-year party. (possible and likely)

❻ Practice drill: 2nd Conditional

🎧 **11.1** Follow the instructions on the Student's CD/Cassette. If necessary, refer to the Listening script on p.87.

 Pocket Book p. 3

Pronunciation   Contractions in 1st and 2nd Conditional sentences

🎧 **11.2** Listen to the examples. Notice the contractions.

a We won't win the contract if the reports aren't ready.
b If we got there early, we'd get the best tickets.

🎧 **11.3** Listen to the sentences. Write the missing verbs. Some are contractions.

1 We _____ the job if we _____ all weekend.
2 If you _____ tired, you _____ mistakes.
3 He _____ to work if he _____ more time.
4 If the tickets _____ today, they _____ tomorrow.
5 He _____ us if the brochures _____ ready.
6 If I _____ their faces, I _____ them.
7 I _____ you if I _____ anything.
8 She _____ for help if she _____ a problem.

🎧 **11.3** Listen again and repeat the sentences.

City description: Collocations

1 Complete the collocations with the words in the box.

> attractions ~~centre~~ language shopping
> capital companies manufacturing

1 financial *centre*
2 _____ industries
3 _____ arcades
4 official _____
5 cultural _____
6 _____ city
7 multi-national _____

2 Complete the article. Use the collocations from **1**.

Stockholm is the _____ [1] of Sweden. It is one of the world's most beautiful cities, with 14 small islands and 54 bridges. In the Old Town there are attractive hotels and restaurants, and you can find lots of elegant shops in the _____ [2]. There are also many _____ [3] in Stockholm including 150 museums and art galleries, and 70 theatres. Over 100 languages are spoken in the city but Swedish is, of course, the _____ [4].

Stockholm is the _____ [5] of Sweden – many business deals take place in the city. The _____ [6] important to Stockholm's economy are engineering, information technology, and computing. Several _____ [7] like Ikea and Electrolux have their headquarters there.

City description: Opposite adjectives

3 Write the opposites of these adjectives.

1 efficient *inefficient*
2 dull _____
3 uninteresting _____
4 modern _____
5 wide _____
6 impressive _____
7 beautiful _____
8 important _____

4 Complete the sentences. Use adjectives from **3**.

1 A *traditional* Christmas market takes place in the Old Town every December.
2 The bus system in the city is very _____ – buses often arrive late.
3 Visitors don't like to look at the _____ buildings in the industrial part of the town.
4 The city is _____ in the evening – many bars, restaurants, and clubs are open until midnight or later.
5 Stockholm is an _____ place to visit – there are a lot of unusual things to do and see.
6 Cars are too big to drive up the old, _____ streets in the city centre.

Social responses

Write responses to the guests' questions and comments at a party. Use the phrases in the box.

> Congratulations!
> Thanks. I'll have an orange juice.
> Thank you. That would be very nice.
> Please do.
> Don't worry.
>
> Really!
> Don't mention it.
> Yes, here you are.
> I'm sorry to hear that.
> It's Sally. Sally Cross.

A May I join you?

B _____ 1

C I'm sorry. I didn't catch your name.

D _____ 2

E Can I get you a drink?

F _____ 3

G Could you pass the water, please?

H _____ 4

C Thank you for all your help this week.

E _____ 5

B Can I get you some more champagne?

A _____ 6

G My mother is in hospital at the moment.

D _____ 7

B I'm sorry. I've spilt some wine.

C _____ 8

F He's a film director, you know.

A _____ 9

C I've just passed my driving test!

E _____ 10

🎧 **11.4** Listen to the complete conversations and check your answers.

🎧 **11.5** Listen and repeat the responses on the Student's CD/Cassette.

 Pocket Book p. 21

UNIT 12

❶ Present Simple passive

Complete the text. Use the Present Simple passive form of the verbs in brackets.

Cognac

Cork _is used_ _____ [1] (use) by the wine and spirits industries for 93% of wine stoppers. Stoppers _____ [2] (need) for other drinks, like sherry and brandy.

The finest brandies – cognac and armagnac – _____ [3] (make) in France. Cognac is the most famous and it _____ [4] (sell) all over the world.

Cognac, like armagnac, _____ [5] (name) after the area where it _____ [6] (produce). The region of Cognac is north of Bordeaux. There, the grapes _____ [7] (grow) in large vineyards. Twenty thousand wine growers _____ [8] (employ) in the industry.

Over 150 million bottles of cognac _____ [9] (export) from France each year. The brandy _____ [10] (enjoy) most of all by Europeans and Americans.

❷ Present Simple active or passive

Underline the correct verb form.

How cognac is produced

- The wine growers _pick_ / _are picked_[1] the grapes in the autumn.

- The grape juice _heats_ / _is heated_[2] twice to produce a clear, 'eau de vie'*.

- The eau de vie _puts_ / _is put_[3] into special oak barrels for a number of years.

- The oak _chooses_ / _is chosen_[4] for the aroma* and colour that it _gives_ / _is given_[5] to the eau de vie.

- After several years, eaux de vie of different ages and from different parts of Cognac _bring_ / _are brought_[6] together and the final cognac _creates_ / _is created_[7].

- A three-star cognac _contains_ / _is contained_[8] eaux de vie as young as two and a half years.

- The finest cognac _produces_ / _is produced_[9] from eaux de vie as old as fifty years.

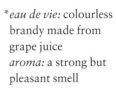

*_eau de vie_: colourless brandy made from grape juice
aroma: a strong but pleasant smell

❸ Past Simple passive

Change the active sentences to Past Simple passive sentences.

The Early History of Cognac

12th century: They established local wine production in Cognac.

Local wine production was established in Cognac. _____ 1

14th century: They developed a wine trade between France and Holland.

_____ 2

16th century: They imported wine products in the form of brandy.

_____ 3

They added water to the brandy in Holland.

_____ 4

They sold the new drink as 'brandywine'.

_____ 5

17th century: They put the 'brandywine' in oak barrels.

_____ 6

The oak improved the quality of the 'brandywine'.

_____ 7 by the oak.

They called the new drink 'cognac'.

_____ 8

❹ Present Perfect passive

Complete the sentences in the Kristala Glass factfile. Use the Present Perfect passive form of the verbs in brackets.

K

Kristala Glass factfile

- Kristala glass *has been produced* 1 (produce) in the Czech Republic for over 150 years.
- Cognac bottles _____ 2 (make) by the company since 1920.
- The bottles _____ 3 (import) by wine producers in France for over seventy years.
- Crystal glass _____ 4 (use) by the company to make cognac glasses since 1946.
- The glasses _____ 5 (sell) all over Europe for almost fifty years.
- A new design for the traditional cognac glass _____ 6 (create) at the factory this year.

❺ Future passive

EurAd is organizing a new advertising campaign for Kristala Glass in Germany. Look at the notes and write sentences about when things will happen. Use the Future passive form.

Kristala Glass Launch Schedule

June	Prepare the script for the Kristala TV advert
20 July	Make the TV advert at the EurAd studios, Dusseldorf
15 September	Hold a press conference at Hotel Adlon, Berlin
26 September	Invite journalists to the Kristala exhibition at the Frankfurt Trade Fair
October	Launch the Kristala TV campaign on RTV
November	Put follow-up adverts in consumer magazines

1 *The script for the Kristala TV advert will be prepared in June.*

2 _____

3 _____

4 _____

5 _____

6 _____

❻ Practice drills: Passive sentences

 12.1, 12.2, 12.3 Follow the instructions on the Student's CD/Cassette. If necessary, refer to the Listening scripts on pp.88–89.

> **Pocket Book p. 9**

Pronunciation   Linking

Read the sentences aloud. Join the words you think are linked.

1 Cognac is named after its region.

2 The town and its region are near Bordeaux.

3 The grapes are grown all over the region.

4 The fruit is picked in the month of September.

5 The juice is turned into a clear eau de vie.

6 This is put into special oak barrels.

7 The oak adds colour and aroma.

12.4 Listen and repeat the sentences.

Word building

❶ Complete the table.

Noun	Adjective	Noun	Adjective
anger	_angry_	_____	hungry
centre	_____	industry	_____
comfort	_____	knowledge	_____
_____	commercial	_____	noisy
_____	economical	_____	political
fashion	_____	_____	profitable
_____	healthy	value	_____

❷ Complete the sentences. Use the correct nouns and adjectives from **❶**.

1 Sales have increased this year so we have made a _profit_ of €900,000.

2 The older employees are _____ about traditional glass-making methods.

3 There are a lot of factories and warehouses in the _____ area of the city.

4 The _____ of our house has increased by £10,000 since January.

5 I haven't been ill for ten years – I'm a very _____ person.

6 I hope to work for the government, so I am going to study _____ at university.

7 The main banks and businesses are located in the _____ of the city.

❸ Complete the pairs of sentences. Use the words in the box.

> careful / careless   hopeful / hopeless   ~~powerful / powerless~~
> harmful /harmless   painful / painless   useful / useless

1 a The new director is very _powerful_ and makes all the decisions in the company.

  b People in poor countries often feel _powerless_ to change their lives.

2 a Please be _____ when you drive to work – the roads are very icy.

  b I made a lot of _____ mistakes in the sales report so I had to do it again.

3 a My tooth is _____, so I'm going to visit the dentist this afternoon.

  b The treatment is _____ – you won't feel any discomfort.

4 a These machines are old and don't work any more – they're _____ to us.

  b The information you gave me was very _____ for my presentation.

5 a The interview was difficult, so he isn't _____ he'll get the job.

  b The future of the company is _____ – sales are poor and we can't pay our suppliers.

6 a Don't throw the chemicals in the rubbish – they're _____ to the environment.

  b Don't worry! The dog is _____ and won't hurt you.

Thanking for hospitality. Saying goodbye

EurAd's Alexa Brandt has driven Milos Zeman, Kristala's Director, to the airport after the Berlin press conference. Complete the conversation. Use the phrases in the box.

> I really must be going.   It was really enjoyable.
> See you on the 26th.   have a good trip back.
> Thank you very much for your hospitality.   I'm glad you enjoyed it.
> I'm looking forward to our next meeting

MILOS	Thanks for driving me to the airport.
ALEXA	Not at all. It was the least I could do after all your hard work this week.
MILOS	Well, it hasn't all been hard work, and you've been very kind.
	_____ 1
ALEXA	You're very welcome. _____ 2
MILOS	I certainly did. _____ 3
	Ah, look. They're calling my flight to Prague now.
	_____ 4
ALEXA	Yes, of course. Well, _____ 5
	at the Frankfurt Trade Fair in September.
MILOS	Me, too. _____ 6
ALEXA	Yes. So, goodbye for now, and
	_____ 7
MILOS	Thanks. Goodbye.

 12.5 Listen to the conversation and check your answers.

 12.6 Listen and repeat the sentences on the Student's CD/Cassette.

◆ Pocket Book p. 21

Listening scripts

Unit 1

🎧 **1.1** p.9

Practice drill 1   **Present Simple questions**

Make questions from the sentences.

Example 1
She lives in Madrid.
Does she live in Madrid?

Example 2
They make good wine.
Do they make good wine?

Now, you do the same.
She lives in Madrid.
Does she live in Madrid?
They make good wine.
Do they make good wine?
He works in Paris.
Does he work in Paris?
They like the new restaurant.
Do they like the new restaurant?
It takes place every year.
Does it take place every year?
They sell all over Europe.
Do they sell all over Europe?

🎧 **1.2** p.9

Practice drill 2   **Present Simple questions**

Make questions from the sentences.

Example 1
They're busy.
Are they busy?

Example 2
He's a director.
Is he a director?

Now, you do the same.
They're busy.
Are they busy?
He's a director.
Is he a director?
You're busy.
Are you busy?
It's a magazine.
Is it a magazine?
She's an interpreter.
Is she an interpreter?
They're translators.
Are they translators?

🎧 **1.3** p.9

Pronunciation   **Intonation of questions**

Repeat the questions.
1 Who is Vinexpo for?
2 Does it finish at 1.00?
3 Are you interested in going?
4 What do you do?
5 How many exhibitors come?
6 Do you use English at work?
7 Are you from Sydney?
8 What date is the next Vinexpo?
9 Which part of Italy are you from?
10 Do you import Italian wine?

🎧 **1.4** p.11

Focus on functions   **Introductions, greetings, and goodbyes**

Listen to the four conversations.

Conversation 1

C=Charles, K=Kristal, D=David
C David, let me introduce you to Kristal Schwartz. Kristal, this is David Porter. David, this is Kristal Schwartz.
K Hello. Pleased to meet you.
D Pleased to meet you, too.

Conversation 2

W=Mr West, R=Mrs Rice
W Excuse me, but are you Mrs Rice?
R Yes, that's right.
W May I introduce myself? I'm Michael West.
R How do you do?
W How do you do?

Conversation 3

A=Alan, L=Lucy
A Hello, Lucy. How are you?
L Fine, thanks, Alan. Good to see you again.
A Nice to see you, too. How's the family?
L They're all very well. How's life?
A Oh, not too bad, thanks, but very busy.

Conversation 4

B=Barbara, P=Patrick
B Patrick, I must go now – my flight is at 5.00.
P Well, it was very nice meeting you.
B I really enjoyed meeting you, too.
P I look forward to seeing you in Madrid.
B I do, too. See you next month.

🎧 1.5 p.11

Introductions, greetings, and goodbyes

Repeat the phrases.
Let me introduce you to Mr Smith.
How's life?
How do you do?
Pleased to meet you.
Good to see you again.
May I introduce myself?
Please call me John.
I'd like to introduce you to an old colleague.
It was very nice meeting you.
I look forward to seeing you in Berlin.

Unit 2

🎧 2.1 p.15

Practice drill 1 **Present Continuous questions**

Make questions from the sentences.

Example 1
He's talking to a supplier.
Is he talking to a supplier?

Example 2
They're travelling to Paris.
Are they travelling to Paris?

Now, you do the same.
He's talking to a supplier.
Is he talking to a supplier?
They're travelling to Paris.
Are they travelling to Paris?
She's reading the report.
Is she reading the report?
He's working at home.
Is he working at home?
She's writing a letter.
Is she writing a letter?
They're having a meeting.
Are they having a meeting?

🎧 2.2 p.15

Practice drill 2 **Present Continuous negative answers**

Give negative answers to the questions.

Example 1
Is she writing the report?
No, she isn't.

Example 2
Are you working at home?
No, I'm not.

Now, you do the same.
Is she writing the report?
No, she isn't.
Are you working at home?
No, I'm not.

Are they having a meeting?
No, they aren't.
Is he seeing a customer?
No, he isn't.
Are you reading the report?
No, I'm not.
Is she talking to the manager?
No, she isn't.

🎧 2.3 p.15

Pronunciation **Strong and weak forms of *do* and *does***

Repeat the sentences.
1 Do you know the place?
2 Yes, I do.
3 Where does he work?
4 Does he work in Paris?
5 Yes, he does.
6 When do they leave?
7 Do they often fly?
8 Yes, they do.

🎧 2.4 p.17

Focus on functions **Making contact**

Listen to the conversation.
R=Receptionist, G=George, D=David
R Good afternoon. Global Travel. How can I help you?
G Hello. Can I speak to Emma Norton, please?
R Who's calling, please?
G It's George Kolasinski.
R Thank you. Hold the line, please. I'll put you through to her office.
G Thank you.
D Emma Norton's phone. David Lawson here. Can I help you?
G Oh, this is George Kolasinski. Could I speak to Emma, please?
D I'm sorry, she's away today.
G Oh, no! I need to speak to her – it's quite important.
D Perhaps I can help you.
G Thank you. Could you give her a message?
D Yes, of course.
G Could you ask her to call me tomorrow morning?
D Yes, certainly. Could you tell me your name again, please?
G It's Kolasinski. George Kolasinski.
D Can you spell that, please?
G It's K-O-L-A-S-I-N-S-K-I.
D And can I have your number?
G It's 0-1-6-5-7, 3-double two-5-8-9-0.
D Right. So that's Mr George Kolasinski on 0-1-6-5-7, 3-double two-5-8-9-0.
G That's it. Thanks very much. Goodbye.
D Goodbye.

🎧 **2.5** p.17

Focus on functions **Making contact**

Repeat the phrases.
Can I speak to Emma, please?
Who's calling, please?
Hold the line, please.
I'm sorry, she's away today.
Could you give her a message?
Can you ask her to call me?
Can I take a message?
Could you tell me your name again, please?
Could you spell that, please?
Can I have your number?

Unit 3

🎧 **3.1** p.21

Practice drill 1 **Past Simple negative sentences**

Make negative sentences.

Example 1
We ate at a restaurant.
(at home)
We didn't eat at home.

Example 2
We visited an art gallery.
(the city museum)
We didn't visit the city museum.

Now, you do the same.
We ate at a restaurant.
(at home)
We didn't eat at home.
We visited an art gallery.
(the city museum)
We didn't visit the city museum.
We went to a club.
(to the cinema)
We didn't go to the cinema.
We flew from New York.
(from Washington)
We didn't fly from Washington.
We stayed in a hotel.
(with friends)
We didn't stay with friends.

🎧 **3.2** p.21

Practice drill 2 **Past Simple questions**

Make questions from the sentences.

Example 1
They arrived on time.
Did they arrive on time?

Example 2
The train left at midday.
Did the train leave at midday?

Now, you do the same.
They arrived on time.
Did they arrive on time?
The train left at midday.
Did the train leave at midday?
She called him last night.
Did she call him last night?
The visitors came to the office.
Did the visitors come to the office?
He told them the news.
Did he tell them the news?

🎧 **3.3** p.21

Pronunciation **-*ed* endings in the Past Simple**

Repeat the verbs.
asked, complained, decided, faxed, lasted, picked, played, reported, returned, stopped, travelled, visited

🎧 **3.4** p.23

Focus on functions **Welcoming a visitor**

Listen to the conversation.
P=Paola, T=Takashi
P   Good to see you again, Takashi, and welcome to Italy.
T   Thank you, Paola. It's nice to be here.
P   Is this your first visit to this part of Italy?
T   Yes, it is. I only know Rome.
P   So ... how did you get here?
T   Well, I flew to Rome on Saturday and stayed two nights there. Then I took the train from Rome to Milan this morning.
P   Did you have a good journey?
T   Yes, thanks. The train was very comfortable.
P   Did you have any problems finding us?
T   No, none at all. Your directions were fine.
P   How was your stay in Rome?
T   Very pleasant, thanks. I did some sightseeing and some shopping, of course.
P   Good. And I'm pleased you're seeing Milan in the sun. Spring has come early this year. What was the weather like in Tokyo when you left?
T   Well, actually, it was very wet there. So I came to Milan at the right time!

🎧 **3.5** p.23

Focus on functions **Welcoming a visitor**

Repeat the questions.
Did you have a good journey?
Did you have any problems finding us?
What was the weather like in Tokyo?
What was your journey like?
How was your flight?
How was your stay?
How did you get here?
Is this your first visit here?

Unit 4

🎧 **4.1** p.27

Practice drill 1 Questions with *going to*

Make questions from the sentences.

Example 1
She's going to fly to Paris.
Is she going to fly to Paris?

Example 2
They're going to have a meeting.
Are they going to have a meeting?

Now, you do the same.
She's going to fly to Paris.
Is she going to fly to Paris?
They're going to have a meeting.
Are they going to have a meeting?
It's going to be hot tomorrow.
Is it going to be hot tomorrow?
They're going to meet for dinner.
Are they going to meet for dinner?
He's going to find a new job.
Is he going to find a new job?

🎧 **4.2** p.27

Practice drill 2 Short answers with *going to*

Answer the questions.

Example 1
Am I going to get the job?
(yes)
Yes, you are.

Example 2
Is she going to write a report?
(no)
No, she isn't.

Now, you do the same.
Am I going to get the job?
(yes)
Yes, you are.
Is she going to write a report?
(no)
No, she isn't.
Are they going to work this evening?
(no)
No, they aren't.
Is he going to catch the train?
(yes)
Yes, he is.
Am I going to find the answer?
(no)
No, you aren't.
Are we going to send the letter?
(yes)
Yes, we are.
Is it going to rain tomorrow?
(no)
No, it isn't.

🎧 **4.3** p.27

Pronunciation Word stress

Repeat the countries and nationalities.

America	American
Japan	Japanese
Australia	Australian
Belgium	Belgian
Canada	Canadian
China	Chinese
Egypt	Egyptian
Europe	European
Germany	German
Hungary	Hungarian
India	Indian
Italy	Italian
Kuwait	Kuwaiti
Pakistan	Pakistani
Poland	Polish
Portugal	Portuguese

🎧 **4.4** p.29

Focus on functions Staying at a hotel

Listen to the three conversations.

Conversation 1

R=Receptionist, C=Caller
R Cape Coral Hotel. Good morning. How may I help you?
C Oh, hello. I'd like to book a single room.
R Yes, certainly, Madam. When is that for?
C For Wednesday the 16th of June.
R And for how many nights?
C For one night.
R OK. And could I have your name, please?
C Yes, it's Paola Giacalone.
R Fine. I'll reserve a room for you immediately.

Conversation 2

R=Receptionist, G=Guest
G Hello. My name's Paola Giacalone. I have a reservation.
R Oh, yes. Good evening, Madam. Welcome to the Cape Coral Hotel. Could you fill in this form, please?
G Sure.
R Can you sign here, please? ... Thank you. Here's your keycard.
G Thanks. Could I have an early-morning call?
R Yes, of course. At what time?
G At 6.45, please.

Conversation 3

R=Receptionist, G=Guest
G Good morning. Could I have my bill, please?
R Certainly, Madam. Did you have anything from the minibar last night?
G No, nothing.
R Fine. Here's your bill.
G Thank you.
R How would you like to pay?

G Can I pay by credit card?
R Yes, that's fine.
G Good. I'll pay by Mastercard then.

🎧 **4.5** p.29

Focus on functions   **Staying at a hotel**

Repeat the phrases.
I'd like to book a single room.
For Wednesday the 16th of June.
For two nights.
I have a reservation.
Could I have an early-morning call?
Could I have my bill, please?
Can I pay by credit card?
Good. I'll pay by Mastercard then.

Unit 5

🎧 **5.1** p.33

Practice drill 1   **Questions with *any***

Make questions from the sentences.

Example 1
He had some free time.
Did he have any free time?

Example 2
They chose some books.
Did they choose any books?

Now, you do the same.
He had some free time.
Did he have any free time?
They chose some books.
Did they choose any books?
She got some money.
Did she get any money?
They bought some presents.
Did they buy any presents?
He wrote some reports.
Did he write any reports?

🎧 **5.2** p.33

Practice drill 2   **Sentences with *much* and *many***

Answer the questions.

Example 1
Did they have any tomatoes?
They had some, but not many.

Example 2
Did they have any bread?
They had some, but not much.

Now, you do the same.
Did they have any tomatoes?
They had some, but not many.
Did they have any bread?
They had some, but not much.

Did they have any wine?
They had some, but not much.
Did they have any melons?
They had some, but not many.
Did they have any potatoes?
They had some, but not many.
Did they have any coffee?
They had some, but not much.

🎧 **5.3** p.33

Pronunciation   **Word stress**

Listen to the examples.
fitness, machine, calories

Repeat the words.
fitness, culture, leisure, training
machine, advice, amount, result
calories, energy, oranges, studio

🎧 **5.4** p.35

Focus on functions   **At a restaurant**

Listen to the two conversations.

Conversation 1

H=Host, G=Guest
H Right. Let's order.
G Oh, I'm afraid I don't know anything about Japanese food. What do you recommend?
H Well, for a starter, what about *yakitori*?
G *Yakitori*? What's that?
H It's small kebabs, with pieces of chicken and a vegetable called *naganegi*.
G Yes, I'd like to try that.
H Now, how about the main course? The *shabushabu* is usually very good here.
G What's *shabushabu*?
H It's thin pieces of beef and various vegetables which we cook at the table.
G Fine. I'll have that.

Conversation 2

H=Host, G=Guest
G Mm. This drink is delicious, but it's quite strong. What is it?
H *Umeshu*. It's a type of spirits made from barley and plums. Would you like some more?
G Thanks. Just a little.
H Now, what about a dessert?
G Thank you, but I couldn't eat any more.
H Are you sure? Would you like coffee, then?
G Yes, that would be very nice. Thank you for a wonderful meal.
H You're welcome.

🎧 **5.5** p.35

Focus on functions   At a restaurant

Repeat the phrases.
What do you recommend?
The meat is usually excellent here.
Yes, I'd like that.
Would you like some more wine?
Thanks. Just a little.
What about the main course?
How about a dessert?
Thank you, but I really couldn't eat any more.
Thank you for a wonderful meal.

Unit 6

🎧 **6.1** p.39

Practice drill 1   Comparative sentences

Give negative answers to the questions.

Example 1
Is Africa as big as Asia?
No, Asia's bigger.

Example 2
Is Washington as interesting as New York?
No, New York's more interesting.

Now, you do the same.
Is Africa as big as Asia?
No, Asia's bigger.
Is Washington as interesting as New York?
No, New York's more interesting.
Is Paris as hot as Cairo?
No, Cairo's hotter.
Is Luxembourg as expensive as Monaco?
No, Monaco's more expensive.
Are the Alps as high as the Andes?
No, the Andes are higher.
Is Belgium as crowded as Hong Kong?
No, Hong Kong's more crowded.

🎧 **6.2** p.39

Practice drill 2   Superlative sentences

Make superlative sentences.

Example 1
The river is very long.
Yes, it's the longest river in the world.

Example 2
The airline is very reliable.
Yes, it's the most reliable airline in the world.

Now, you do the same.
The river is very long.
Yes, it's the longest river in the world.
The airline is very reliable.
Yes, it's the most reliable airline in the world.
The train is very fast.
Yes, it's the fastest train in the world.

The city is very exciting.
Yes, it's the most exciting city in the world.
The aeroplane is very big.
Yes, it's the biggest aeroplane in the world.
The country is very expensive.
Yes, it's the most expensive country in the world.

🎧 **6.3** p.39

Pronunciation   The /ə/ sound

Repeat the phrases.
as easy as
taller than
less expensive than
the newest
the most reliable
as late as
better than
more famous than
the quickest
the most famous

🎧 **6.4** p.41

Focus on functions   Making arrangements

Listen to the conversation.

S=Steve, M=Maria
S   Is that Maria Pertini?
M   Yes. Speaking.
S   Hello, this is Steve Holmes. I'm flying to Milan later this week, so could we arrange a meeting to discuss the Elco project?
M   Yes, of course. Let me see. I can see you on Thursday or Friday. When are you free?
S   Is Friday morning possible for you?
M   Yes, that's OK. Shall we say 10 o'clock?
S   Yes, 10 a.m. suits me fine.
M   Ah! Wait a moment. No, I'm afraid I'm busy then. I've got a meeting with a client. Could we arrange another time?
S   Yes, of course. When would be convenient for you?
M   How about Friday afternoon?
S   What time would suit you?
M   How about two o'clock?
S   Yes, that's fine.
M   Good. See you on Friday afternoon at 2.00.

🎧 **6.5** p.41

Focus on functions **Making arrangements**

Repeat the phrases.
Could we arrange a meeting?
When would be convenient for you?
What time would suit you?
Is Friday morning possible for you?
How about two o'clock?
Shall we say next Tuesday?
Yes, 10 a.m. suits me fine.
No, I'm afraid I'm busy then.
Could we arrange another time?
See you on Friday afternoon at two.

Unit 7

🎧 **7.1** p.45

Practice drill 1 **Present Perfect Simple questions**

Make questions from the sentences.

Example 1
They've been to Milan.
Have they been to Milan?

Example 2
She's sent the report.
Has she sent the report?

Now, you do the same.
They've been to Milan.
Have they been to Milan?
She's sent the report.
Has she sent the report?
You've received a bonus.
Have you received a bonus?
He's forgotten the meeting.
Has he forgotten the meeting?
Prices have increased.
Have prices increased?

🎧 **7.2** p.45

Practice drill 2 **Present Perfect Simple and Past Simple answers**

Give positive answers to the questions.

Example 1
Have they started a new business?
(last year)
Yes, they have. They started it last year.

Example 2
Has he read the report?
(yesterday)
Yes, he has. He read it yesterday.

Now, you do the same.
Have they started a new business?
(last year)
Yes, they have. They started it last year.
Has he read the report?
(yesterday)
Yes, he has. He read it yesterday.
Has she written the memo?
(on Monday)
Yes, she has. She wrote it on Monday.
Have they received the invoice?
(this morning)
Yes, they have. They received it this morning.
Has he finished the project?
(last week)
Yes, he has. He finished it last week.

🎧 **7.3** p.45

Pronunciation **Past Simple and Present Perfect Simple**

Listen to the sentences. Which tense do you hear?
1 I've applied for Ben's job.
2 I asked for more time.
3 We had a visitor.
4 We've heard the news.
5 They've worked in Africa.
6 They went to Nigeria.
7 I've finished the project.
8 I faxed the report.

🎧 **7.4** p.47

Focus on functions **Opinions and suggestions**

Listen to the two conversations.

Conversation 1

A=Anne, C=Carl
A I'm happy in my job, but I'd like a new challenge. Any ideas on what I can do?
C Why not travel round the world for a year?
A I don't just want to travel. I'd like to really get to know another country and learn about their culture.
C Well, why don't you get a job abroad for a year or two? You could help people in the Third World and learn about their culture, too.
A Yes, that's a good idea. I'll talk to my boss about it.

Conversation 2

Y=Yvette, A=Anne
Y What did your boss say?
A He's given me unpaid leave for a year.
Y That's good of him! What do you plan to do?
A I'm going to work for Oxfam and help build new schools in Guatemala. What do you think about that?
Y In my opinion, it's a bad career move. You can return to your job, but I think you're going to lose opportunities for promotion.
A I'm not sure about that. The company hopes to expand into Latin America. My boss says it could be very useful experience.

7.5 p.47

Focus on functions   Opinions and suggestions

Repeat the phrases.
Any ideas on what I can do?
What do you think about that?
Why don't you get a job abroad?
Why not travel around the world?
I'm not sure about that.
Yes, that's a good idea.
In my opinion, it's a bad career move.
I think that's a really great idea.
I certainly agree with that.
I'm sorry, but I disagree.

Unit 8

8.1 p.50

Practice drill 1   Questions with *should* and *have to*

Make questions from the sentences.

Example 1
You should get a car.
Should I get a car?

Example 2
I have to work on Sunday.
Do you have to work on Sunday?

Now, you do the same.
You should get a car.
Should I get a car?
I have to work on Sunday.
Do you have to work on Sunday?
They should leave now.
Should they leave now?
He has to answer the question.
Does he have to answer the question?
You should call the police.
Should I call the police?
She has to go home early.
Does she have to go home early?

8.2 p.51

Pronunciation   Sentence stress and emphasis

Listen to the conversations.

B=Bill, L=Lisa
B   I think we should go by train.
L   *Well, I think we should go by plane.*
B   Tony may get here by 9.00.
L   *He has to get here before 9.00.*
B   Susie says we should try that new café.
L   *But Tania says we shouldn't.*
B   It's important to be honest with them.
L   *It's important not to tell them all the facts.*
B   You have to wear suits for formal meetings.
L   *But you don't have to wear suits in the office.*

Repeat Lisa's replies.
Well, I think we should go by plane.

He has to get here before 9.00.
But Tania says we shouldn't.
It's important not to tell them all the facts.
But you don't have to wear suits in the office.

8.3 p.53

Focus on functions   Invitations

Listen to the conversation.

D=Dieter, L=Lucy, H=Helga
D   How was your first week, Lucy?
L   You do things differently here, but everyone has been very helpful.
D   Good. We're all going out for a meal after work. Would you like to join us?
L   I'd love to, but I'm afraid I can't. You see, I promised my new neighbours I'd go to their barbecue at 6.00.
H   Oh, that's a pity. … I'm going into town tomorrow morning. Would you join me there for lunch? I could show you the old castle in the afternoon.
L   Thanks a lot, but I'm meeting an old college friend in Munich tomorrow. Sorry!
H   No problem. What about Sunday? Some of us are going on a trip to the Bodensee – that's Lake Constance in English. How about joining us?
L   That sounds nice.
D   Yes, it's beautiful at this time of year, so why don't you come with us?
L   Are you sure?
H   Yes, of course. You're very welcome.
L   Thank you. I'd enjoy that very much.
D   Good. We'll pick you up at 8.30 on Sunday morning.

8.4 p.53

Focus on functions   Invitations

Repeat the phrases.
Why don't you come with us?
Thank you. I'd enjoy that very much.
Would you like to join us?
I'd be delighted to accept.
Would you join me for lunch?
Thanks a lot, but I'm meeting a friend.
I'd love to, but I'm afraid I can't.
How about joining us tomorrow?

Unit 9

9.1 p.57

Practice drill 1   Present Perfect Continuous questions

Ask questions about the sentences.

Example 1
He's travelling.
How long has he been travelling?

Example 2
Sales are increasing.
How long have sales been increasing?

Now, you do the same.
He's travelling.
How long has he been travelling?
Sales are increasing.
How long have sales been increasing?
They're talking.
How long have they been talking?
It's raining.
How long has it been raining?
They're having a meeting.
How long have they been having a meeting?
She's writing her report.
How long has she been writing her report?

🎧 **9.2** p.57

Practice drill 2   **Present Perfect Continuous answers**

Give positive answers to the questions.

Example 1
Is he working in Marseilles?
(since last month)
Yes, he's been working in Marseilles since last month.

Example 2
Are they learning Japanese?
(for a long time)
Yes, they've been learning Japanese for a long time.

Now, you do the same.
Is he working in Marseilles?
(since last month)
Yes, he's been working in Marseilles since last month.
Are they learning Japanese?
(for a long time)
Yes, they've been learning Japanese for a long time.
Is it raining?
(since midday)
Yes, it's been raining since midday.
Are they playing golf?
(for two hours)
Yes, they've been playing golf for two hours.
Is he visiting customers?
(since Monday)
Yes, he's been visiting customers since Monday.

🎧 **9.3** p.58

Pronunciation   **Word stress**

Listen to the examples.
importer, company, competitor

Repeat the words.
importer, production, investment, translator
company, organize, industry, operate
competitor, development, distributor, industrial

🎧 **9.4** p.59

Focus on functions   **Offers and requests**

Listen to the two conversations.

Conversation 1

H=Helen, T=Tony

H   I have to check in for my flight to Chicago in an hour, so could you print out this report and distribute it? I don't have time.

T   Yes, certainly. Shall I drive you to the airport?

H   That's very kind of you, but it's more important for you to be here.

T   Well, would you like me to call a taxi?

H   Thank you. I'd appreciate that. Could we say ten minutes from now?

Conversation 2

H=Helen, S = Sandra

H   Hi, Sandra, I'm arriving in Chicago at 16.45 local time. Would you be able to meet me at the airport? Then we could talk on the way to the hotel.

S   I'm sorry, but that's not possible. I have an important meeting.

H   OK, no problem. Would you mind sending a car to meet me?

S   Yes, of course. I'll arrange that right now. And if you like, I could meet you later at the hotel.

H   Great. Let's meet at 8.00 and have dinner together.

S   That's fine. See you soon, and have a good trip.

🎧 **9.5** p.59

Focus on functions   **Offers and requests**

Repeat the phrases.
Shall I drive you to the airport?
Would you like me to call a taxi?
If you like, I could meet you at the hotel.
Could you print out this report?
Would you be able to meet me?
I'm sorry, but that's not possible.
Yes, of course.
Thank you. I'd appreciate that.
That's very kind of you, but I can manage.
Would you mind sending a car?

Unit 10

🎧 **10.1** p.63

Practice drill   **1st Conditional**

Make sentences.

Example 1
(start now / finish early)
If we start now, we'll finish early.

Example 2
(don't start soon / finish late)
If we don't start soon, we'll finish late.

Now, you do the same.
(start now / finish early)
If we start now, we'll finish early.

(don't start soon / finish late)
If we don't start soon, we'll finish late.
(travel at night / save a lot of money)
If we travel at night, we'll save a lot of money.
(don't travel at night / the tickets cost more)
If we don't travel at night, the tickets will cost more.
(get better jobs / earn more money)
If we get better jobs, we'll earn more money.
(don't get better jobs / always have money problems)
If we don't get better jobs, we'll always have money problems.

🎧 **10.2** p.63

Pronunciation   *will* and *'ll*

Listen to the conversation.
R=Reporter, E=Engineer
R   It's a fantastic project. Do you think it'll succeed?
E   Oh, yes, we're sure it will.
R   Will the wind farm be very big?
E   Yes, it'll be about 36 kilometres long.
R   Will people be able to see it from the coast?
E   Yes, they will, but not easily. The turbines'll be a long way from the coast.
R   I suppose there'll be damage to wildlife.
E   No, we don't think there will. We're making sure there'll be very little.

🎧 **10.3** p.63

Pronunciation   *will* and *'ll*

Repeat phrases from the conversation.
Do you think it'll succeed?
We're sure it will.
Will the wind farm be very big?
It'll be 36 kilometres long.
Will people be able to see it?
Yes, they will.
The turbines'll be a long way …
… there'll be damage.
We don't think there will.
There'll be very little.

🎧 **10.4** p.65

Focus on functions   **Asking for information**

Listen to the conversation.
K=Kate Dee, J= Julia Carr
K   So, you want to spend the summer at an environmental work camp. Is that right?
J   Yes. I'd like some information about camps in Spain or Portugal.
K   What about Sungrow Desert Technology? They're based in Cambridge, but they have a big environmental project in the south of Spain.
J   That sounds interesting. Could you tell me how to contact them?
K   I'll look that up. Right, you can contact them by post or by email.
J   Can you tell me their email address?
K   It's sungrow@clara.net.

J   Could you repeat that, please?
K   Of course. It's sungrow@clara.net.
J   Do you know what kind of work they do?
K   I'm afraid I don't have much information about that. It just says that they work on farming techniques for very dry regions. I suggest you find out from their website. It's sundestec.org.uk.
J   Right, I've got that. Thanks for your help.
K   You're very welcome.

🎧 **10.5** p.65

Focus on functions   **Asking for information**

Repeat the phrases.
I'd like some information about camps in Spain.
Do you know what they do?
Could you tell me how to contact them?
I'm sorry, but I don't have any information.
I'll look that up.
Let me check for you.
Could you repeat that, please?
Can you tell me their email address?
Right, I've got that.
Could you say that again?

Unit 11

🎧 **11.1** p.69

Practice drill   **2nd Conditional**

Answer the questions.
Example 1
If you had a year off, what would you do?
(travel round the world)
If I had a year off, I'd travel round the world.

Example 2
If you travelled round the world, where would you go first?
(go to Australia)
If I travelled round the world, I'd go to Australia.

Now, you do the same.
If you had a year off, what would you do?
(travel round the world)
If I had a year off, I'd travel round the world.
If you travelled round the world, where would you go first?
(go to Australia first)
If I travelled round the world, I'd go to Australia first.
If you went to Australia, what city would you visit first?
(visit Sydney first)
If I went to Australia, I'd visit Sydney first.
If you visited Sydney, how would you spend your time?
(spend my time at Bondi Beach)
If I visited Sydney, I'd spend my time at Bondi Beach.
If you spent your time at Bondi Beach, what would you do there?
(go surfing every day)
If I spent my time at Bondi Beach, I'd go surfing every day!

🎧 **11.2** p.69

Pronunciation   **Contractions in 1st and 2nd Conditional sentences**

Listen to the examples.
We won't win the contract if the reports aren't ready.
If we got there early, we'd get the best tickets.

🎧 **11.3** p.69

Pronunciation   **Contractions in 1st and 2nd Conditional sentences**

Listen to the sentences. Then repeat.
1 We'd finish the job if we worked all weekend.
2 If you're tired, you'll make mistakes.
3 He wouldn't drive to work if he had more time.
4 If the tickets don't come today, they'll arrive tomorrow.
5 He'll email us if the brochures aren't ready.
6 If I saw their faces, I'd remember them.
7 I won't call you if I don't hear anything.
8 She wouldn't ask for help if she didn't have a problem.

🎧 **11.4** p.71

Focus on functions   **Social responses**

Listen to the conversations.
1 A May I join you?
   B Please do.

2 C I'm sorry. I didn't catch your name.
   D It's Sally. Sally Cross.

3 E Can I get you a drink?
   F Thanks. I'll have an orange juice.

4 G Could you pass the water, please?
   H Yes, here you are.

5 C Thank you for all your help this week.
   E Don't mention it.

6 B Can I get you some more champagne?
   A Thank you. That would be very nice.

7 G My mother is in hospital at the moment.
   D I'm sorry to hear that.

8 B I'm sorry. I've spilt some wine.
   C Don't worry.

9 F He's a film director, you know.
   A Really!

10 C I've just passed my driving test!
   E Congratulations!

🎧 **11.5** p.71

Focus on functions   **Social responses**

Repeat the responses.
Please do.
Thanks. I'll have a whisky.
Don't mention it.
Thank you. That would be very nice.

I'm very sorry to hear that.
Really!
Yes, here you are.
Don't worry.
It's James. James Turner.
Congratulations!

Unit 12

🎧 **12.1** p.75

Practice drill 1   **Present Simple passive**

Make passive sentences.

Example 1
They make armagnac in France.
Armagnac is made in France.

Example 2
They manufacture cars in Japan.
Cars are manufactured in Japan.

Now, you do the same.
They make armagnac in France.
Armagnac is made in France.
They manufacture cars in Japan.
Cars are manufactured in Japan.
They produce sherry in Spain.
Sherry is produced in Spain.
They write software in India.
Software is written in India.
They grow olives in Italy.
Olives are grown in Italy.
They build ships in Korea.
Ships are built in Korea.

🎧 **12.2** p.75

Practice drill 2   **Past Simple passive**

Make passive sentences.

Example 1
She didn't finish the report.
The report wasn't finished.

Example 2
They didn't order the books.
The books weren't ordered.

Now, you do the same.
She didn't finish the report.
The report wasn't finished.
They didn't order the books.
The books weren't ordered.
We didn't read the memo.
The memo wasn't read.
He didn't sell the apartments.
The apartments weren't sold.
You didn't answer the letter.
The letter wasn't answered.
I didn't check the figures.
The figures weren't checked.

🎧 12.3 p.75

Practice drill 3 **Present Perfect passive**

Make passive sentences.

Example 1
Has she booked the rooms?
Have the rooms been booked?

Example 2
Have they agreed the price?
Has the price been agreed?

Now, you do the same.
Has she booked the rooms?
Have the rooms been booked?
Have they agreed the price?
Has the price been agreed?
Has he found the invoices?
Have the invoices been found?
Have you sent the email?
Has the email been sent?
Has she sold the computers?
Have the computers been sold?
Has he signed the contract?
Has the contract been signed?

🎧 12.4 p.75

Pronunciation **Linking**

Repeat the sentences.
1 Cognac is named after its region.
2 The town and its region are near Bordeaux.
3 The grapes are grown all over the region.
4 The fruit is picked in the month of September.
5 The juice is turned into a clear eau de vie.
6 This is put into special oak barrels.
7 The oak adds colour and aroma.

🎧 12.5 p.77

Focus on functions **Thanking for hospitality.**
Saying goodbye

Listen to the conversation.
M=Milos, A=Alexa
M Thanks for driving me to the airport.
A Not at all. It was the least I could do after all your hard work this week.
M Well, it hasn't all been hard work, and you've been very kind. Thank you very much for your hospitality.
A You're very welcome. I'm glad you enjoyed it.
M I certainly did. It was really enjoyable. Ah, look. They're calling my flight to Prague now. I really must be going.
A Yes, of course. Well, I'm looking forward to our next meeting at the Frankfurt Trade Fair in September.
M Me, too. See you on the 26th.
A Yes. So, goodbye for now, and have a good trip back.
M Thanks. Goodbye.

🎧 12.6 p.77

Focus on functions **Thanking for hospitality.**
Saying goodbye

Repeat the sentences.
Thank you very much for your hospitality.
I'm glad you enjoyed it.
It was really enjoyable.
I'm looking forward to our next meeting.
I really must be going.
I've had a wonderful time.
I'm glad you found it interesting.
I must be off.
See you on the 26th.
Have a good trip back.

Answer key

Unit 1

Language focus

1
1 *run*	6 manage
2 comes	7 produce
3 knows	8 know
4 is	9 help
5 has	10 persuades

2
1 *comes*	6 don't work
2 *doesn't come*	7 produce
3 is	8 runs
4 doesn't live	9 helps
5 live	10 manages

3
1 *Do you have*	5 Are you
2 Do you want	6 do I need
3 Does it start	7 do we have
4 does it finish	

4 1 *What* 2 Where 3 When 4 Who
5 How many 6 Why 7 What

5
1 *Are you Signora Leone-Bell?*
2 Are you from Sydney?
3 Which part of Italy are you from?
4 What do you do?
5 … do you import Italian wine?
6 Do you want to taste it?
7 What grape do you use?
8 Do you know the name?
9 Is he your husband?

7 🎧 **1.1, 1.2** (Refer to Listening scripts, p.78.)

Pronunciation

1 ↘ 2 ↗ 3 ↗ 4 ↘ 5 ↘
6 ↗ 7 ↗ 8 ↘ 9 ↘ 10 ↗

Wordpower

1
1 *Surname*	8 Date of birth
2 Forename(s)	9 Place of birth
3 Home address	10 Nationality
4 Post code	11 Passport no.
5 Telephone	12 Country of residence
6 Mobile	13 Signature
7 Email address	

2
1 *comb*	4 pen	7 watch
2 keys	5 diary	8 driving licence
3 credit cards	6 wallet	9 mobile phone

Focus on functions

1 let me introduce you
2 Pleased to meet you.
3 May I introduce myself?
4 How do you do?
5 Good to see you again.
6 How's life?
7 it was very nice meeting you.
8 I look forward to seeing you in Madrid.

Unit 2

Language focus

1
1 *sell*	7 employs
2 takes	8 works
3 seems	9 find
4 have	10 send
5 speak	11 deals
6 want	12 returns

2
answer-**ing**	arriv(e)-**ing**	begin-**n-ing**
growing	*becoming*	*cutting*
starting	handling	forgetting
staying	reducing	getting
trying	taking	stopping
working	using	travelling

3
1 *is becoming*	6 is growing
2 are travelling	7 are handling
3 is reducing	8 are answering
4 are getting	9 are trying
5 is beginning	10 are working

4
1 *The company is expanding its activities in India.*
2 The company isn't employing new staff in the Bangalore office.
3 They're opening new offices in Chennai and Mumbai.
4 The company isn't planning to expand overseas at the present time.
5 Sales of the company's home computers are increasing.
6 They're not making changes to their software programs.
7 The Managing Director is having a lot of meetings with IBM.

5
1 *Are you enjoying*	5 are you doing
2 Is he doing	6 Are you telling him
3 are you phoning	7 Are you working
4 are you visiting	

6
1 *live*	6 are trying
2 run	7 deals
3 imports	8 is looking
4 is growing	9 is visiting
5 are rising	10 are having

7 🎧 **2.1, 2.2** (Refer to Listening scripts, p.79.)

Pronunciation

1 *b* 2 *a* 3 b 4 b 5 a 6 b 7 b 8 a

Wordpower

1 1 work 2 have 3 do 4 make
2
1 *make an appointment*	5 have lunch
2 do a good job	6 make a phone call
3 work part-time	7 do some research
4 work flexitime	8 have a holiday

3 Not in work: *out of work*, retired, unemployed
Working hours: flexitime, full-time, part-time
Time away from work: holidays, maternity leave, paternity leave, sick leave
Work activities: emails, meetings, reports, phone calls
Pay: sick pay, wages, salary

Focus on functions

1 Can I speak to
2 Who's calling, please?
3 Hold the line, please.
4 I'm sorry, she's away today.
5 Could you give her a message?
6 Could you ask her to call me
7 Could you tell me your name again
8 Can you spell that, please?
9 can I have your number?

Unit 3

Language focus

1
1	*worked*	7	arrived
2	did … visit	8	called
3	started	9	wanted
4	needed	10	Did … agree
5	did … stay	11	changed
6	Did … return	12	suggested

2
1	*grew*	6	chose	11	had
2	helped	7	became	12	accepted
3	ran	8	won	13	decided
4	went	9	made	14	open
5	began	10	broke	15	created

4
1 *Did you start SG Intercafés alone?*
2 Were there any big problems?
3 Did the bank help much?
4 Did the business grow fast after that?
5 When did you start your company?
6 Why did you call it Forest Housing?
7 What problems did you have?

5
1 *Where did you go?*
2 Which supplier did you visit?
3 Who did you talk to?
4 Why was she unhappy about our last payment?
5 How did you deal with the problem?
6 What possible new suppliers did you visit?
7 Which supplier sent me information?
8 When did the supplier send me information (last year)?
9 Where did he meet me?
10 How much discount did he offer?

6 🎧 **3.1, 3.2** (Refer to Listening scripts, p.80.)

Pronunciation

		/d/	/t/	/ɪd/
1	asked		✓	
2	complained	✓		
3	decided			✓
4	faxed		✓	
5	lasted			✓
6	picked		✓	
7	played	✓		
8	reported			✓
9	returned	✓		
10	stopped		✓	
11	travelled	✓		
12	visited			✓

Wordpower

1
1	*swimming*	5	tennis	9	judo
2	badminton	6	table tennis	10	aerobics
3	basketball	7	fitness training	11	yoga
4	squash	8	weight training	12	rollerblading

2 do (weight training, judo, aerobics, yoga)
go (climbing, diving, riding, jogging)
play (squash, golf, table tennis, football)

3 1 *café* 2 restaurant 3 wine bar
4 cinema club 5 concerts

Focus on functions

1 Is this your first visit
2 how did you get here?
3 Did you have a good journey?
4 Did you have any problems finding us?
5 How was your stay
6 What was the weather like

Unit 4

Language focus

1
1	*'m flying*	5	'm writing
2	'm meeting	6	'm making
3	'm giving	7	'm not doing
4	'm interviewing		

2
1	*are we holding*	4	people are going
2	Are you inviting	5	Are you leading
3	is it taking	6	am I talking

3
1 *We're holding the seminar at the Cape Coral Hotel in Nassau.*
2 No, I'm also inviting all training staff.
3 It's taking place from 2–4 June.
4 Ninety-seven people are going to the seminar.
5 No, I'm leading it with Mark Grady (of Global Training).
6 You're talking to everyone at the start.

4
1 *I'm going to visit Bay Street and do my shopping there.*
2 We're going to try some of Nassau's wonderful restaurants.
3 She's going to swim with the dolphins near Grand Bahama Island.
4 They're going to relax on the beautiful Paradise Island beaches.
5 I'm going to see the spectacular Atlantis Superboat Challenge.
6 He's going to dive with a local guide to see the beautiful underwater world.
7 We're going to explore the fantastic rainforest in Lucayan National Park.

5
1 *are you going to open*
2 Is it going to be
3 are you going to offer
4 are you going to compete
5 people are going to work
6 are the builders going to start
7 is the building work going to take
8 is the whole project going to cost
a 7 b 8 c 2 d 6 e 3 f 1 g 5 h 4

6 🎧 **4.1, 4.2** (Refer to Listening scripts, p.81.)

Pronunciation

America   American
Japan   Japanese
Australia   Australian
Belgium   Belgian
Canada   Canadian
China   Chinese
Egypt   Egyptian
Europe   European
Germany   German
Hungary   Hungarian
India   Indian
Italy   Italian
Kuwait   Kuwaiti
Pakistan   Pakistani
Poland   Polish
Portugal   Portuguese

Wordpower

1 1 *double room, twin room*
2 full-board, half-board
3 luggage, suitcase
4 shower, bath
5 bill, receipt

2 1 *multi-line phone*
2 computer / fax point
3 satellite TV
4 safe
5 minibar
6 24-hour room service
7 business centre
8 conference facilities
9 fitness centre
10 swimming-pool
11 cocktail bar
12 restaurants

Focus on functions

1 I'd like to book a single room.
2 For Wednesday 16 June.
3 For one night.
4 I have a reservation.
5 Could I have an early-morning call?
6 Could I have my bill, please?
7 Can I pay by credit card?
8 Good. I'll pay by Mastercard then.

Unit 5

Language focus

1 1 *good health*
2 regular training
3 machines
4 equipment
5 advice
6 time
7 Research
8 results
9 hard work
10 Relaxation
11 information

2 1 a *times* b *time*
2 a exercise b exercises
3 a foods b food
4 a fruit b fruits
5 a life b lives
6 a noise b noises
7 a sports b sport
8 a businesses b business

3 1 *a lot of* 2 many 3 much 4 A lot of
5 many 6 much 7 a lot of 8 many

4 1 *How much* 5 How much
2 Only a little 6 Only a little
3 How many 7 How many
4 Only a few 8 Only a few

5 1 *some* 2 any 3 some 4 a 5 some
6 some 7 any 8 a 9 some 10 a
11 Some 12 any

6 🎧 **5.1, 5.2** (Refer to Listening scripts, p.82.)

Pronunciation

culture   advice   energy
leisure   amount   oranges
training   result   studio

Wordpower

1 1 *salmon* 2 red pepper 3 cut 4 chicken
5 peach 6 mineral water 7 cutlet 8 cheese

2 1 Grill 2 Fry 3 Boil 4 Roast

3 1 d 2 f 3 c 4 h 5 a 6 g 7 b 8 e

Focus on functions

1 What do you recommend?
2 Yes, I'd like to try that.
3 how about the main course?
4 Would you like some more?
5 Thanks. Just a little.
6 Thank you, but I couldn't eat any more.
7 Thank you for a wonderful meal.

Unit 6

Language focus

1 1 *lower* 2 nearer 3 further 4 better
5 cheaper 6 bigger 7 higher 8 longer

2 1 *JumpJet has the best website.*
2 JumpJet has the cheapest fares.
3 SkyLine has the biggest discount for online bookings.
4 JumpJet has the quickest check-in time.
5 BestFlight has the longest delays.
6 JumpJet has the newest planes.
7 SkyLine has the smallest amount of leg room.

3 1 *BestFlight's website is as good as SkyLine's.*
2 *BestFlight's fares aren't as cheap as JumpJet's.*
3 JumpJet's discount for online bookings is as big as BestFlight's.
4 SkyLine's check-in time isn't as quick as BestFlight's.
5 JumpJet's delays are as long as SkyLine's.
6 SkyLine's planes aren't as new as JumpJet's.
7 BestFlight's amount of leg room isn't as small as SkyLine's.

4 1 *less expensive than* 4 less comfortable than
2 more efficient than 5 more helpful than
3 less reliable than

5 1 *KDM's fares are the most expensive.*
Atlantica's fares are the least expensive.
2 Transworld's check-in systems are the most efficient.
North-East's check-in systems are the least efficient.
3 North-East's schedules are the most reliable.
Atlantica's schedules are the least reliable.

4 KDM's seats are the most comfortable.
  Atlantica's seats are the least comfortable.
5 Atlantica's staff are the most helpful.
  Transworld's staff are the least helpful.

6 1 *the fastest*   7 the most important
      2 the most famous   8 the most difficult
      3 the most beautiful   9 the highest
      4 the most exciting   10 the most expensive
      5 the best   11 the richest
      6 the earliest   12 the saddest

7 🎧 **6.1, 6.2** (Refer to Listening scripts, p.83.)

Pronunciation

as easy as   taller than   less expensive than

the newest   the most reliable

as late as   better than   more famous than

the quickest   the most famous

as easy as   taller than   less expensive than
the newest   the most reliable
as late as   better than   more famous than
the quickest   the most famous

Wordpower

1 1 *hand-luggage*   4 seat-belts
      2 duty-free shop   5 flight attendant
      3 overhead locker

2 1 *officer*   5 seat
      2 screen   6 luggage
      3 card   7 security
      4 desk   8 passport

3 1 luggage trolley   5 boarding card
      2 check-in desk   6 security announcement
      3 window seat   7 security checks
      4 departures screen

Focus on functions

1 When are you free?
2 Is Friday morning possible for you?
3 10 a.m. suits me fine.
4 No, I'm afraid I'm busy then.
5 Could we arrange another time?
6 When would be convenient for you?
7 How about two o'clock?
8 See you on Friday afternoon at 2.00.

Unit 7

Language focus

1 1 *started*   5 collected   9 went
      2 *met*   6 sent   10 became
      3 formed   7 came
      4 began   8 saw

2 1 *have included*   6 has provided
      2 has been   7 has trained
      3 has worked   8 have improved
      4 has organized   9 has made
      5 have helped   10 have built

3 Infinitive   Past Simple   Past Participle
      break   broke   *broken*
      buy   bought   bought
      cost   *cost*   cost
      drink   drank   drunk
      eat   ate   *eaten*
      fall   *fell*   fallen
      forget   forgot   forgotten
      find   *found*   found
      give   gave   *given*
      have   had   *had*
      hear   heard   heard
      hit   *hit*   hit
      know   knew   known
      lose   lost   *lost*
      put   put   put
      rise   *rose*   risen
      sell   sold   *sold*
      shut   shut   shut
      understand   *understood*   understood
      wear   wore   *worn*

      Irregular verbs
      meet   met   met
      begin   began   begun
      send   sent   sent
      come   came   come
      see   saw   seen
      go   went   gone
      become   became   become
      be   was   been
      make   made   made
      build   built   built

4 1 *have become*   5 have received
      2 have grown   6 were often, often hurt
      3 started   7 have continued
      4 have borrowed   8 have finally begun

5 1 *established*   7 sold
      2 wanted   8 did
      3 has encouraged   9 has developed
      4 have worked   10 has sold
      5 set   11 has changed
      6 learned

6 1 *How long has your workshop been in business?*
      2 Has the economic crisis affected your business?
      3 Have you had financial problems?
      4 Where have you sold your products up to now?
      5 Have you thought about selling outside Indonesia?

7 🎧 **7.1, 7.2** (Refer to Listening scripts, p.84.)

Pronunciation

1 *PPS*   2 *PS*   3 PS   4 PPS   5 PPS   6 PS
7 PPS   8 PS

Wordpower

1 1 *from, to*   2 in, to   3 of, in   4 at   5 by
      6 in, to   7 by   8 of, in, from, to

2 Noun   Adverb
      a decrease   dramatically
      a fall   sharply
      an improvement   slightly
      an increase   steadily
      a rise

3
1. *have fallen sharply*
2. *has been a dramatic rise*
3. has been a steady decrease
4. have fallen sharply
5. has improved steadily
6. have decreased slightly
7. has been a dramatic improvement
8. has been a slight increase

Focus on functions

1. Any ideas on
2. Why not travel round
3. why don't you get a job abroad
4. Yes, that's a good idea.
5. What do you think about that?
6. In my opinion,
7. I think
8. I'm not sure about that.

Unit 8

Language focus

1
1	*have to*	6	has to
2	important to	7	shouldn't
3	may	8	might
4	don't have to	9	should
5	important not to	10	may not

2
1. *don't have to, have to*
2. don't have to, have to
3. should, shouldn't
4. may not, may
5. 's important not to, 's important to
6. might, might not

3
1. *You have to wear a business suit at meetings.*
2. You should make small talk at the beginning of meetings.
3. You don't have to exchange business cards with each other.
4. You may do business on the golf course.
5. You have to learn the job titles of everyone in the company.
6. You shouldn't give expensive gifts to your host.

4
1. (correct)
2. *You should read this book.*
3. (correct)
4. Might they fly home tomorrow?
5. (correct)
6. They don't have to go.
7. Andreas may leave the company.
8. Should he go to Milan?
9. She has to call me back tomorrow.
10. Felipe should arrange a meeting.

5 🎧 **8.1** (Refer to Listening script, p.85.)

Pronunciation

1. *Well, I think we should go by plane.*
2. He has to get here before 9.00.
3. But Tania says we shouldn't.
4. It's important not to tell them all the facts.
5. But you don't have to wear suits in the office.

Wordpower

1
1	*adaptability*	5	ambition
2	important	6	creativity
3	successful	7	organized
4	success	8	organization

2 Armand: *ambitious*, efficient, impatient, insensitive
Maria: creative, sociable, unpunctual, disorganized
Jason: reliable, honest, unambitious, unsociable

Focus on functions

1. Would you like to join us?
2. I'd love to, but I'm afraid I can't.
3. Would you join me
4. Thanks a lot, but
5. How about
6. why don't you come with us?
7. Thank you. I'd enjoy that very much.

Unit 9

Language focus

1
1	*has become*	7	was
2	founded	8	has remained
3	have developed	9	decided
4	have increased	10	has continued
5	grew	11	have produced
6	needed	12	appeared

2
1	*have been making*	5	has been learning
2	has had	6	has designed
3	has developed	7	has shown
4	has been producing	8	has been working

3
1. a *He has been writing reports since 1 p.m.*
   b He has written two reports so far.
2. a He has been speaking for 45 minutes.
   b He has given three presentations this week.
3. a She has been learning English for five years.
   b She has visited the UK twice this year.
4. a She has been driving round town all morning.
   b She has seen four customers so far.
5. a He has been working in the wine industry since he left college.
   b He has worked for three different companies since he left college.

4
1. *for* 2. in 3. for 4. since 5. since
6. for 7. at 8. in 9. at

5
1. *Sales have been rising for four months.*
2. Susan has been travelling since 20 August.
3. Silvie and Tomas have been business partners for … years.
4. Blanca-Maria has been working in Poland since February.
5. James has been away for five days.

7 🎧 **9.1, 9.2** (Refer to Listening scripts, pp.85, 86.)

Wordpower

1
Verb	Noun (activity, thing)	Noun (person)
compete	*competition*	competitor
consume	consumption	consumer
develop	development	*developer*
distribute	distribution	*distributor*
economize	economy	*economist*
industrialize	*industry*	industrialist
invest	investment	investor
operate	operation	operator
organize	organization	*organizer*
translate	translation	translator

Pronunciation

• • •   • • •   • • • •

investment   industry   development
production   operate   distributor
translator   organize   industrial

2 1 *free-market* 2 countries 3 management
4 industrial 5 goods 6 mass

3 1 consumer goods   4 developing countries
   2 management skills   5 industrial development
   3 free-market economy   6 mass production

Focus on functions

1 could you
2 Shall I drive you
3 That's very kind of you, but
4 would you like me to call
5 Thank you. I'd appreciate that.
6 Would you be able to meet me
7 I'm sorry, but that's not possible.
8 Would you mind
9 Yes, of course.
10 if you like, I could

Unit 10

Language focus

1 1 *Global warming will change the world's climate.*
   2 Summers will become hotter and drier.
   3 Higher temperatures will melt the Arctic ice.
   4 Sea levels will rise by up to seven metres.
   5 People in coastal areas will lose their homes.
   6 Cities in coastal areas will disappear under water.

2 1 *Do you think you will live abroad?*
   2 Do you think you will work from home?
   3 Do you think you will do your shopping online?
   4 Do you think you will have more leisure time than today?
   5 Do you think you will learn a new language?
   6 Do you think you will send all your letters by email?
   7 Do you think you will do more for the environment than now?
   a 4 b 3 c 6 d 7 e *1* f 5 g 2

3 1 *Where will the wind farm be?*
   2 When will the wind farm start to operate?
   3 How many wind turbines will they construct?
   4 How big will the wind turbines be?
   5 Will the wind farm be very expensive to build?
   6 How much electricity will it produce?
   7 Will there be more offshore wind farms?

4 1 *won't* 2 'll 3 'll 4 won't
   5 'll 6 'll 7 won't 8 'll

5 1 *If Mark agrees with Kay, they'll buy an Ecostar.*
   2 *They won't get an XS4 if Kay wins the argument.*
   3 If they choose an Ecostar, it'll be expensive to buy.
   4 They'll spend a lot on fuel if they decide to get an XS4.
   5 If they choose an XS4, there won't be much room for their baby.
   6 They'll have a lot of storage space if they get an Ecostar.
   7 If they buy an Ecostar, they'll help the environment.

6 🎧 **10.1** (Refer to Listening script, p.86.)

Pronunciation

1 *'ll* 2 *will* 3 Will 4 'll 5 Will 6 will 7 'll 8 'll
9 will 10 'll

Wordpower

1 *The reception desk is on the left of the reception area.*
2 The sales office is on the right of the reception area.
3 Kay is on the sofa.
4 Mark is behind the sofa.
5 The coffee table is in front of Kay.
6 The rubbish bin is under the coffee table.
7 The coffee machine is between the photocopier and the water cooler.
8 The phone is next to the computer keyboard.
9 The showroom sign is above the showroom entrance.
10 Mark's and Kay's new car is in the showroom.

Focus on functions

1 I'd like some information about
2 Could you tell me how
3 I'll look that up.
4 Can you tell me
5 Could you repeat that, please?
6 Do you know what
7 I'm afraid I don't have much information about that.
8 Right, I've got that.

Unit 11

Language focus

1 1 *communicated*   7 relied
   2 *would lose*   8 wouldn't be able
   3 provided   9 wasn't / weren't
   4 wouldn't have   10 would use
   5 travelled   11 arrived
   6 would get   12 wouldn't complain

2 1 *If our public transport system was efficient, more people would use it.*
   2 *The system would be more efficient if we integrated the buses and trains.*
   3 If we introduced a light-rail system, it would reduce car traffic.
   4 If commuters used a single ticket for all journeys, they could change easily from one route to another.
   5 Public transport would be more popular if we reduced the cost.
   6 If we introduced a congestion charge, fewer motorists would drive into the city.
   7 People would leave their cars outside the city if we provided free car parks and buses.
   8 If more people used bikes, this would reduce traffic congestion.
   9 More people would cycle to work if we created safe cycle lanes.
   10 If we encouraged car-sharing schemes, there would be a lot less traffic.

4 1 *built, would it be*
   2 *would live, decided*
   3 had, would there be
   4 lived, would it take
   5 would people do, started
   6 Would the building be, hit
   7 agreed, would the building work take
   a 5 b 7 c 4 d *1* e 2 f 6 g 3

5 1 *If I get the salary rise that I want, I'll …*
   2 If my company offered me the top job in its New York office, …
   3 If some friends at work invite me for a meal on Friday, …
   4 If I won two round-the-world air tickets, …
   5 If I have some free time next month, …
   6 If I met an old school friend on holiday, …
   7 If someone in my English class suggests an end-of-year party, …

6 🎧 **11.1** (Refer to Listening script, p.87.)

Pronunciation

1 'd finish, worked
2 're, 'll
3 wouldn't drive, had
4 don't come, 'll arrive
5 'll email, aren't
6 saw, 'd remember
7 won't call, don't hear
8 wouldn't ask, didn't have

Wordpower

1 1 *centre*
   2 manufacturing
   3 shopping
   4 language
   5 attractions
   6 capital
   7 companies

2 1 capital city
   2 shopping arcades
   3 cultural attractions
   4 official language
   5 financial centre
   6 manufacturing industries
   7 multi-national companies

3 1 *inefficient*
   2 lively
   3 interesting
   4 traditional
   5 narrow
   6 unimpressive
   7 ugly
   8 unimportant

4 1 *traditional*
   2 inefficient
   3 ugly
   4 lively
   5 interesting
   6 narrow

Focus on functions

1 Please do.
2 It's Sally. Sally Cross.
3 Thanks. I'll have an orange juice.
4 Yes, here you are.
5 Don't mention it.
6 Thank you. That would be very nice.
7 I'm sorry to hear that.
8 Don't worry.
9 Really!
10 Congratulations!

Unit 12

Language focus

1 1 *is used*
   2 are needed
   3 are made
   4 is sold
   5 is named
   6 is produced
   7 are grown
   8 are employed
   9 are exported
  10 is enjoyed

2 1 *pick*
   2 is heated
   3 is put
   4 is chosen
   5 gives
   6 are brought
   7 is created
   8 contains
   9 is produced

3 1 *Local wine production was established in Cognac.*
   2 A wine trade was developed between France and Holland.
   3 Wine products were imported in the form of brandy.
   4 Water was added to the brandy in Holland.
   5 The new drink was sold as 'brandywine'.
   6 The 'brandywine' was put in oak barrels.
   7 The quality of the 'brandywine' was impoved …
   8 The new drink was called *Cognac*.

4 1 *has been produced*
   2 have been made
   3 have been imported
   4 has been used
   5 have been sold
   6 has been created

5 1 *The script for the Kristala TV advert will be prepared in June.*
   2 The TV advert will be made at the EurAd studios, Dusseldorf on 20 July.
   3 A press conference will be held at the Hotel Adlon, Berlin on 15 September.
   4 Journalists will be invited to the Kristala exhibition at the Frankfurt Trade Fair on 26 September.
   5 The TV campaign will be launched on RTV in October.
   6 Follow-up adverts will be put in consumer magazines in November.

6 🎧 **12.1, 12.2, 12.3** (Refer to Listening scripts, pp.88–89.)

Pronunciation

1 *Cognac‿is named‿after‿its region.*
2 The town‿and‿its region‿are near Bordeaux.
3 The grapes‿are grown‿all‿over the region.
4 The fruit‿is picked‿in the month‿of September.
5 The juice‿is turned‿into a clear‿eau de vie.
6 This‿is put‿into special‿oak barrels.
7 The oak‿adds colour‿and‿aroma.

Wordpower

1
Noun	Adjective
anger	*angry*
centre	central
comfort	comfortable
commerce	*commercial*
economy	*economical*
fashion	fashionable
health	*healthy*
hunger	*hungry*
industry	industrial
knowledge	knowledgeable
noise	*noisy*
politics	*political*
profit	*profitable*
value	valuable

2 1 *profit*
   2 knowledgeable
   3 industrial
   4 value
   5 healthy
   6 politics
   7 centre

3 1 a *powerful*
   2 a careful
   3 a painful
   4 a useless
   5 a hopeful
   6 a harmful
   b *powerless*
   b careless
   b painless
   b useful
   b hopeless
   b harmless

Focus on functions

1 Thank you very much for your hospitality.
2 I'm glad you enjoyed it.
3 It was really enjoyable.
4 I really must be going.
5 I'm looking forward to our next meeting
6 See you on the 26th.
7 have a good trip back.